ONE MAN'S SPIRITUAL AWAKENING TO SEXUALITY

THE ADVENTUROUS CHRONICLES OF

WOMB MAN

A NOVEL BY

DONIVAN WEI COLTRANE

POETRY BY

KAI HERU

First Edition—E-Book Release, 2011
Book Cover Design by: Robert Deane
Avima Graphics, Detroit, MI
avimadesign@gmail.com

Library of Congress Cataloging-in-Publication Data
Gardner, Duan 1966 -
      The Adventurous Chronicles of Womb Man, Vol. 1
      One Man's Spiritual Awakening to Sexuality
      Duan Ivan Gardner– 1st ed.
      ISBN 978-0-9823479-2-8

POETRY BY KAI HERU

Mitchell & Morgan does not participate in, endorse, or have any au- thority or responsibility concerning private business transactions between our authors and the public. All mail addressed to the au- thor is forwarded but the publisher cannot, unless specifically in- structed by the authors, give out an address or phone number. Any internet references contained in this work are current at publication time, but the publisher cannot guarantee that a specific location will continue to be maintained.   Please refer to publisher's website for links to authors' website and other sources.

Mitchell & Morgan Publishing
PO Box 35100, Detroit, Michigan 48235
www.mitchellandmorganpublishing.com

TABLE OF CONTENTS

Warning!!!

A Personal Reflection   2

Introduction: Ready or Not Here I.....   5

A Star Is Born   7

Lil' Man?   9

Growin Up, Goin' Down   17

The Playa Chronicles   19

     Strange Love 20

     Heaven Is In Me 25

     Perfection 27

     Stay Black 29

Dear Mama   31

Adolescence   34

     Gaze 35

     Irony 36

The Real Deal   39

A Glimpse of Heaven   41

     Her Eyes 43

Jack Pot!   47

     The Cat's Meow 48

Dick Control   54

The Nerve of Some Monsters   61

From Boy To Man   67

TABLE OF CONTENTS

Movin' On   69
    Batteries Included 71
    All Grown Up   73

Fresh Out of the Wrapper   75
Lucy...I'm Home   83
Life Happens   88
    A Bad Marriage 93

Oh, Really Now???   98
By Who??? Girl Bye!   105
    She is Life 109
    Life.....Before Death 111

Let The Games Begin!   115
    Makin' Love 120

Full Speed Ahead   125
Beam Me Up Scotty   127
The Mack Attack   135
Here Comes the Judge   149
....And Away We Go!   150
New Skool   159
Cher-e-e-e-e-e-ery Ba-ya-be!   163
Challenges   172
Trouble In Cherryland   189
    Goin' Off, After What Went On 194

A Personal Reflection   197

WARNING!!!

The writing style(s) you are about to encounter may cause severe 'reading engagement.' Like most writers, I tend to utilize a variety of different energies to rhetorically express myself. Those energies may range from (but are not limited to) emotional, to spiritual, to intellectual, to erotic, to philosophical, to ironic, to (extremely) sarcastic, to plain ol' jiga-boo ghetto ebonic energy. However, it may become a little disconcerting as I amalgamate these styles into, let's say, the same paragraph? So, I just ask that you strap in as we journey thru the passionate depths of my heart, soul and mind.

- DONIVAN WEI COLTRANE

A Personal Reflection...

I'm speaking to you from the future, 2046 A. D. I am now 80 years young and more vibrant and healthy than ever. Even after all these years it feels absolutely wonderful being wealthy...I simply love it! Perfect health and tremendous wealth are always my focus. I'm on a private beach in the Cost Rica Republic enjoying this warm sunny day; reclining and swirling my feet in the sand watching the tide roll in. The sun is directly over my head, so I guess it's about 1 o'clock pm. It's partly cloudy, but the sun is shining brilliantly.

My life is so very complete. I wish for nothing and I want for nothing. I'm enjoying life at its best while enjoying the best of life. Can you believe I still have a six pack stomach and a toned muscular body, sort of like Jack Lalaine was at my age? I still have all of my own teeth and arise with a full erection most mornings. What can I say? Life is wonderful!

It would all be for naught if it wasn't for the most special person in my life. You see, I worship, praise and adore the most magnificently wonderful goddess on the planet...and we just so happen to be married. We're celebrating our 34th anniversary. Wow! You should see her.

Auset is so beautiful. She's turning 67 this year and she's JUST starting to get salt and pepper hair. Auset is slim and petite, yet very curvaceous with the darkest, smoothest complexion you've ever seen. My Queen has a very even skin tone partially because she sun baths every morning...not a wrinkle. The sun has such miraculous effects upon our melanin. Neither of us has aged very much because time has been so very good to us. Talk about fortunate? Most people think we're in our 50's. Younger guys try to "hit on" Auset all the time. I love it!

My Queen stands 5'3" and weighs about 120 pounds. She's slightly bow-legged from the hips down and her small waist and flat stomach accentuate her well-toned, wonderfully symmetric body.

Ahhh, here she comes right now. I love the way the breeze is blowing her sun-dress against her body and between her legs as she walks toward me. I can clearly see the outline of her sensuous figure. Even after all these years, her breasts and butt are still fighting against gravity. That's absolutely unbelievable and a MAJOR plus!

I simply adore rubbing my face against her soft, silky, wavy hair. It's in a curly pony tail today. I love it when she wears it like that. Auset still has the most radiantly beautiful and heart-warming smile I've ever seen and after 34 years it's become even warmer. Her smile always makes me smile. She has big, light-brown, bedroom eyes that speak as expressively as she talks. Auset has a naturally pretty face...so gorgeous. Her neck is youthful and wrinkle-free. I love the detailed outline of her full, roller coaster lips. Her slightly squared jaw and subtly cleft chin are in no way masculine. In fact, Auset is femininity personified...physically, mentally and spiritually.

I kiss my Diva's feet every morning. It's a loving pre-commemorative promise I made to the MOST HIGH for bringing us to-gether. Auset is perfect for me; she's my Soul Mate...the feminine expression of myself...my balance. She lives strictly by the principles of MA'AT and forever expresses the highest fidelity towards me. Auset is a high-energy, high-vibration, highly-ascended conscious woman. She is confident, perseverant and charismatic. Auset simply loves all my innate qualities and characteristics that I cannot change about myself. Yes, she loves my very essence. We're so very happy together! In fact, I never thought I could (consistently and continuously) be so very happy.

I must say, there's absolutely NOTHING more sacred than a woman. She is the beginning of all things and the power behind everything. She is both man's compliment and his Deity. She is the original man who existed millions of years before man was created. She sustains the universe and many holy books are based upon her anatomy. Her voice is the melody of life and her scent is the most alluring perfume. Her mere beauty has broken the strongest of men and the sweetness of her nectar is the weakness of men.

I now have a very clear perception of the goddess concept. However, I must readily admit that I haven't always felt this way, nor have I always embraced and expressed such truths. In fact, it was Auset who helped me discover these and other ultra ma-son-ic principles that took me more than 40 years of preparation to learn and overstand. You've heard the old saying: "When the student is ready the teacher will appear." Well in this example, the student and the teacher are one and the same. The student is my human side and the teacher is my divine self. Sometimes, the teacher is the feminine balance within your masculinity. So, let me take you back to my beginning, to my own Gene-Isis so you can see how far I've come and how much I've transcended.

Introduction

Ready or Not Here I...

First of all, I was born a very sexual being. I mean, I was conceived through sex...the external personification of heterosexation (yeah, it's a word I made up). So, just think about it for a moment...I came into the world with my butt-naked ass sliding through a vagina, and it's not like I wanted to come out. I was simultaneously pushed and pulled from 'da pussy,' and trust me, I've been trying to get back in every since (Lol!). I guess you can say I was quite literally, a motherfucker when I was born. So, my very first experience in the world was oozing head first through a vagina, evicted from my humble abode. It's no wonder I stay so home sick.

Secondly, I was born choking on a mouthful of vaginal fluid and much hasn't changed since then (Lol!). And if that wasn't bad enough, I got spanked on my wet, naked ass (a time-honored tradition that I've since passed on). Now, is that sexual or what? Then, the next thing I knew I was placed upon two breasts and I went straight for the nipples. But what's really interesting is that nobody showed me how to suck. It was a natural phenomenon. I just started sucking and I've never really stopped (old habits are so hard to break). So, I became a damn good sucker very early in life. I guess that's where my oral fixation was initially cultivated.

Every few hours somebody would come and expose my genitals and that's when I'd give 'em my best R. Kelly impression, that special shower of love right in the face...and they loved it! Boy how they'd laugh, actually we both would (maybe that's what got Kelly started). A warm towel and some cool baby powder would soon follow. I had strange women kissing on my face all the time. Some would lift my shirt and kiss my lil' navel while I gazed into their scalp (and even today, it's a wonderful view). Or, they'd place my tiny feet in their mouth. Now, don't think for one minute these happenings didn't have a profound sexual effect upon me, even as an infant. Remember, a baby's mind is like a sponge and they mentally file all that shit. I know I did. However, regardless of how sexually explicit it might appear, these are my humble beginnings and if you're honest with yourself, they're yours too.

Mothers, please take some good advice. Don't parade around naked in front of your sons! That's just some more shit that fucks our little minds up. After you wean them off the breast, cover yo' ass up! You know, dress like a nun (cause ain't nothin' sexy about that...Lol!). Don't you see the way your sons gawk at you? And the way their lil' eyes rove all over your body? You think at age two they're too young to know what they're looking at, Bullshit! By then, we're breast-masters, and that's why we fondle other women's breasts, because at that age we realize we can still get away with it. But, it's a whole new story when we see a naked ass and a hairy crotch. Now THAT is shocking, especially when it's your mother. Don't you realize you're the first naked woman they see? Trust me, while they're sitting there with their mouths hanging open and their pop-eyes poppin,' they're not thinking...got milk? They're thinking, hmmm...now why does it suddenly feel like I'm growing a third leg? Yeah, that first ass and crotch view is forever engrained in our little infant minds. It's from that point on we look at every woman's ass and crotch. That's usually about the time when little boys start touching women's asses, on purpose of course, although we do a fairly decent job of perpetrating the fraud.

I never understood why little boys cry on their first day of Kindergarten with so much brand-new ass to look at. Shit, that alone was worth the price of admission. You also discover that breasts come in all sizes and that little girls don't have any. I don't remember if I cried, but if I did, they were tears of joy. Oh yeah, and you quickly discover you're too old to touch a grown woman's ass without being held accountable. Trust me, they straighten yo' ass out real quick. Then, you find out the distinct difference between ass and booty. Grown women have asses...little girls have booty. Also, ass is at face level, while booty is at the same height as...my thang. Yep, even at five years young, there are certain sexual realities you become keenly aware of. For instance, grabbing a girl from behind and pumping on her booty is a natural phenomenon (sorta like sucking was as a newborn) and how my thang fits so perfectly between booty. I guess that was the origin of how 'da butt' became my favorite body part and still is. You also discover that little girls don't have thangs. That really messed me up when I found that out. In fact, there was nothing down there at all! I was like, "What the hell?" Ok, let me see if I got this straight. Women have breasts, little girls don't. Little boys have thangs, little girls don't. Grown women have ass, but little girls have booty. Yeah, I think I got it. I'm a little genius!

A Star Is Born

I was born under the sign of Pisces, the culmination of all the Zodiac signs. Besides being very sensitive and intuitive, Pisces are also innate artists and it was discovered very early on that I was an extremely artistic being. In 1970, my parents bought my sister an organ for Christmas. My parents took the "Christmas thing" very, very seriously; so my sister and I were always showered with lots of gifts. However, my sister didn't seem very interested in the organ, which sort of disappointed my parents. They damn near begged her to play it, but to no avail. Afterwards, they attempted to sell me on playing the organ. I remember standing on my toes trying to reach the keys and my parents were ecstatic. I was on that organ every chance I got.

There were very few moments of complete silence in our house because music was always playing. My mother was very heavily into jazz - Authentic Jazz, not that watered down bullshit they call Jazz nowadays; the real stuff like Nancy Wilson, Coltrane and Cannonball Atterly. My dad was a Motown Music fanatic and also loved Soul-Music. Well, on a particular night not long after Christmas, there was a song playing and astonishingly, I began fingering the melody of the song on the organ. My mother started screaming like she'd won the lottery. Even at the tender young age of four, I intuitively understood why she reacted that way. It was very phenomenal. I was also utterly impressed with my own ability to play the right keys. My mom called my dad to the living room to show him what she'd witnessed and he went berserk. He started calling relatives and friends on the phone to have them listen. Man, I was so happy to see my dad that excited about me and to see my parents simultaneously happy about anything. The only one who wasn't so jovial was my sister who started crying because of all the attention I was receiving. But in my little mind, I thought... "Hey sis, they gave you the opportunity."

Then, in first grade another artistic side of me was discovered. The art teacher had my class drawing pictures from coloring books. You know those real simplistic pictures that are boldly outlined? Well, the teacher advised us not to trace the pictures, but (of course) many of the children did anyway and once she discovered it, she made them draw it over. I'd already finished my drawing when some of my classmates asked me to draw theirs. I'd drawn two of their pictures when the teacher came to investigate. She scolded me for allegedly tracing my picture and made me start over. I told her that I hadn't traced it, but so many of the other students already had, so she didn't believe me. So, I drew another picture while she scolded my classmates whose pictures I'd drawn. They confessed that I'd also drawn their pictures without tracing.

She took our drawings and placed each of them against the original pictures only to find that they truly hadn't been traced. "That's absolutely impossible," she said. She turned to a more detailed picture and gave me a clean sheet of paper. "Ok, draw this one," she challenged. And she stood there as I drew it. All the other children in the class gathered around. I knew I had the spotlight so I put extra effort into it. Drawing was so easy for me. I didn't understand what the big deal was. Halfway through my drawing she was convinced. "Oh my goodness, this is incredible!" she said, as if I had broken a world record. The bell rang and the teacher dismissed the class but told me to stay as she called my mother.

We lived right down the street from the school so my mom arrived almost as quickly as she was called. My mother initially thought something was wrong, or that I'd done something wrong, until my art teacher offered her some startling news. "I want you to look at these drawings. I gave the children an assignment to draw pictures from coloring books without tracing them and this is what he did." My mom looked at the pictures with an angry expression and retorted, "And he traced the pictures after you told him NOT to?" My mom 'grimmed' me like she was about to smack the shit outta me. Back then you could still get away with that (Lol!). "No, no he didn't trace them, he actually drew them. I didn't believe it myself until I stood there and actually watched him draw it with my own eyes. Your son is an artistic genius!" My mom's expression quickly changed to shock. It sorta reminded me of when I played that song on my sister's organ.

In second grade it was discovered that I was also quite a thespian. I had to be one of the shyest children around but once I was bitten by the stage acting bug, it was a wrap! I'd always clowned around and performed for my family and friends, but never for strangers. My first stage performance was a musical despite the fact that I'd never sang in front of anyone before. Can you imagine? I couldn't believe how I performed on stage while being nervous. It confounded me because I wasn't forced to be in the play; I decided to perform knowing I'd be nervous. I was good, too!

Everybody commented on how advanced my talent was. But it all seemed so natural to me, as if it was in my blood. It was the applause that hooked me. It was like a narcotic! I loved the instant gratification audiences gave. Even back then, receiving the loudest and longest applause was most important to me. Shit, that's what drove my performance. And if all that wasn't enough, later in the third grade I wrote an autobiography which won a city-wide scholastic writing contest. I ended up being honored at a local high school for my effort and achievement. I won third place out of all the elementary schools throughout the entire city of Detroit. My mom was so proud, but by then she was no longer shocked and amazed by my gifts and talents. In fact, she'd become quite nonchalant regarding my artistic gifts. I guess as I got older it became more difficult to remain impressive.

Lil' Man?

Now, for some reason my experiences with the female gender started very early on in life. And although they were very natural occurrences, they were also considered somewhat mal-adaptive in nature. I remember my mom taking my sister and me on a social visit with some friends of our family. That was a very common occurrence back in the early 70's. Our families were well-acquainted and their father was the assistant pastor of the church that we all attended. As a child, there was nothing better than visiting a family with a lot of children and they had seven that ranged in ages. On this particular occasion, there were other families with their children also visiting. So it was really a child's heaven.

In that era, it was customary for adults to socialize separate and apart from children (times sure have changed). After the initial salutations and greetings when the adults embarrassed you by asking a bunch of goofy questions that they already knew the answers to, all the adults gathered in the dining room and began laughing and talking (loudly!) Boy, they really knew how to entertain themselves with good clean fun.

All the children were relegated to the basement, which is what we all anxiously anticipated and we could hardly wait for the cue. The family was very affluent and had what most considered a mini-mansion, or at the very minimum, a big-ass house. We all tore downstairs into their huge basement and started running around like raging maniacs. Our noise level rivaled and oftentimes surpassed the adults upstairs. And every once in a while when our noise level became too overbearing, one of the adults came to the basement door and hollered for us to tone it down. But they never simply asked us to quiet down; that would've been asking a little too much from a bunch of hyperactive children. I was utterly amazed at how patient their parents were about all the ruckus we made. My mother would've BEEN don' whooped our ass way before then! But I guess they were used to it because they had such a big family. After a few hard falls and crying spells, the two children who were younger than me were summoned upstairs because they couldn't stomp with the big dogs.

That left me as the youngest amongst everybody else, who was older than my older sister; I was seven and she was 10. My sister was absolutely in love with the family's youngest son Ronnie, who was her age. After the basement light mysteriously went off a couple of times and my sister and Ronnie were caught kissing, everybody else sort of paired off and followed suit. I'd always had a real crush on Ronnie's older sister Genise. She was gorgeous and well-received by all the guys at church (older and younger than her) because of her soft, gentle, femininely sweet and demure disposition. Genise was about 14 or 15 years young and stood about 5'10". She had the deepest dimples and the widest smile you'd ever wanna see. Her smile always made you smile.

Everyone in both our families (and at church) knew about my lil' crush on Genise and often teased me about it. I hated when they did that because it always made her respond to me, and as a shy child, that embarrassed me. Her family reared her to be a princess. She spoke with a real slow drawl and always told me how cute I was (at church). But I never took her compliments very seriously because I was just a child and as far as I was concerned, she was a grown-ass woman. Considering how I had to strain my neck to look up at her, I never even thought I had a chance with her. Or that I even knew what a 'chance' was (Lol!). But I'd soon discover.

After a few minutes of watching our siblings kissing and watching everybody else pair off, she kneeled down and kissed me on my lips. I didn't skip a beat. I kissed her like I knew what I was doing, and like I was very interested in taking it further, whatever that meant at seven years young. It was all so natural for me too. She grabbed my lil' hand led me to the couch and laid me down.

Now, please don't consider this molestation, c.s.c. (criminal sexual conduct) or even child abuse, because I certainly didn't. Genise was the perfect blend of assertive and gentle and I was in full and complete agreement with everything that was happening. Ironically, I maintained a very adult mindset. When she placed her tongue in my mouth, I naturally reciprocated. When she embraced me and caressed the back of my head as we kissed, I rubbed her huge face and never felt overwhelmed. Somehow, in my seven-year young mind, body and spirit, I felt there was something more we could have explored. I just didn't know what.

When her extra large hand squeezed my lil' butt, I moved my lil' erection against her because it was the natural thing to do. I struggled to stretch my feet down to rub against her gigantic feet, which were at least a size 10 (Lol!). Genise was so impressed by my apparent sophistication, she called me her 'lil' man,' a very coveted title for a lil' boy. It was like heaven, but even better than the one described in the bible because I didn't have to die first to get there. I wished it could've lasted forever. We all listened out for footsteps (upstairs) leading to the basement door, and whenever anyone even walked into the kitchen, Ronnie flicked the light on. Our parents never had a clue of what was going on. Though we stayed for hours, I think we all wished we'd discovered our fun a whole lot sooner. Man, how we hated to leave! On the ride home, my sister and I smiled in silence in the backseat. I truly believed that's where my fondness for older women was cultivated.

During this same period, my neighborhood best friend Thamont had an older cousin named Jackale. She was a tall, slender aggressive girl who was considered fast (hot to trot) by the neighborhood adults. All the older guys in the neighborhood hung around Thamont's house because of Jackale and all her attractive girl cousins (who were also relatively fast). Since my older sister and Jackale's youngest sister Carilyn were best friends, and Thamont and I were best friends, we all hung out at Thamont's house quite a bit. That is, if they weren't all hanging out at our house. And wherever the girls gathered, the neighborhood guys followed.

All the older guys in my neighborhood coveted Jackale, because she was perhaps the (next) girl most likely to "give it up." She was always one of the girls the guys wanted to find whenever they played hide-and-go-get-'em (that's a derivative of the famous game, hide-and-go-seek. However, the object of this game was to fondle and kiss the girl you found or whatever else she allowed you to do). Well at age eight, I was as intimidated by Jackale as I was intrigued by the older guys' attraction to her.

Jackale was actually kinda funny looking to me. I really thought her younger sister Carilyn was the cute one, but she was sort of a tomboy. Jackale had a square little face with real thick lips. Actually, both sisters had slanted eyes and thick lips, but Jackale was a little darker, taller, and bow-legged (from the hips down) which gave her this real sexy vibe. Her skin-tight jeans used to fit so snug inside her crotch that it accentuated her vaginal lips to the point where it created the letter "w" in her crotch.

12

The combination of that with her long legs, aggressive demeanor and fast disposition made her a neighborhood favorite amongst the older guys.

At age eight, I guess I wasn't as attracted to her "package" as I was intimidated by it. Though there was at least a seven-year difference between us, she always looked at me...funny. She used to call me "cutie," and say she was gonna get me. I kinda knew what she meant, but how could I take her seriously with our age difference and my apparent inexperience? Now Thamont and I were mannish in our own right, mimicking the older guys as we fondled girls our age and younger. But Jackale was a real woman for all practical purposes, and I was just a little boy and there was absolutely no question about that.

As time progressed Jackale became more 'hands-on' with me. I actually stopped visiting Thamont's house as often, unless my sister was with me, or a bunch of children were there (which was usually the case). I usually left when my sister did, or as the crowd of children diminished, whether I was ready to leave or not. Sometimes Jackale would run her fingers through my hair and comment on how cute I was, then she would try to touch my thang. Now that didn't sit well with me, because at age eight, I knew my thang was small. Shit, I was eight and it was to be expected, right? But, I definitely didn't want Jackale, for all practical purposes, a big, grown-ass woman, fondling my (small) eight-year-young thang. I was clearly out of my league with her.

I used to often wonder why she ran so fast and hid so carefully whenever she played hide-and-go-get-'em with the older guys. Why didn't she try to touch them like she tried to touch me? Or, allow them to find her so they could kiss, fondle and pump on her? You see, Thamont and I were too young to play, so all we could do was observe and tell the guys where the girls were hiding as they bribed us. We got a lot of money and candy that way and gained brownie points with the older guys. I also noticed Jackale was more aggressive toward me when my sister wasn't around, which told me she knew she was being out-of-pocket.

It got to a point where my sister started noticing how uncomfortable Jackale made me. Now don't get me wrong, I liked all the attention she gave me. I even liked the notoriety I was receiving from the older guys as a result of her attention. Initially, I tried to play it cool like I was playing hard-to-get. But after a while, it was very evident I wasn't playing it cool; I was just scared of her. Jackale's particular kind of attention was just a bit too intense for me at the time. Some of the older guys used to say, "Hey lil' man, stop runnin' from that pussy!"

There were a few times when Jackale grabbed me from behind and gyrated on my butt while trying to grab my thang. That was such a scary and distressing feeling. She was stronger than me and I felt overpowered. If there's one thing I hate to this very day, whether figurative or literal, is the feeling of being trapped, forced or overpowered...without my express permission of course (Lol!). One time, my sister saw me really struggling to get loose from Jackale while telling her to stop! That's when my sister calmly and inconspicuously asked Jackale to let me go without anyone else around us realizing what had happened. There were so many children there the entire event went virtually unnoticed. As time transpired, my sister would ask me to leave with her when she left Thamont's house because she'd become aware of my apparent dilemma.

It seemed like the more uncomfortable I became from Jackale's advances, the more she relished it. She appeared to love torturing me (I think she was a little sadistic). Every time Jackale would get in whispering distance she would always say, "I'm gonna get yo' cute lil' ass." Then one day she just flat out told me, "I'm gon' pump on you, and yo' sister ain't gonna be around to save you either. I'm gon' tie yo' lil' ass down, cover yo' mouth and take it from you and ain't nobody gon' hear you hollering either." I was terrified when she said that. And she was serious, too! I guess you could say she was officially my first stalker. Thamont was there when she said it and he fell out laughing. Maybe he thought it was so harmless and funny because his cousin said it to his best friend. But, being tied down and forced to have a tall, slender, bow-legged aggressive woman with a "w" in her crotch pump on me mercilessly was still a future fantasy at that particular time. I never went to Thamont's house after that, with or without my sister.

Unfortunately, I had to pass Thamont's house every time my mom sent me to the store, which was at least three times a day because back then my mom had a great affinity for cigarettes and Pepsi and never seemed to keep an adequate supply of either. There were a few times Jackale caught me at the store, but I managed to avert her. For weeks I crossed the street and used the other side of the street as an escape route. I'd see and hear her shouting threats from across the street, "I'm gon' eventually catch you!" By then, most of the neighborhood knew about it (thanks to Thamont's big mouth) and many of the teens were trying to help her catch me. Can you imagine that? It had become like a big game to everybody... except me. Sometimes two or three teens would try to hold me while she attempted to cross the street and nab me, but we lived on a very busy street right off the freeway which often times was difficult to cross, so I got away most times.

I managed to avoid Jackale altogether for the duration of the summer. I'd even gotten the nerve to walk down our side of the street, though I usually jogged by Thamont's house there and back. One early afternoon my mom sent me to the store for a gallon of milk. I did my usual look-out measures and jogged past Thamont's house and got to the store safely. I was on my way back carefree and content when suddenly, just as I'd passed Thamont's house, Jackale jumped on my back out of nowhere. It was like she jumped outta the sky 'cause I DAMN sure didn't see where she came from. Imagine that, sexually accosted on a public sidewalk (Lol!).

She took me totally by surprise and I was shocked. There was absolutely nobody around or even outside. I can't recall seeing a single car driving down our very busy street. Isn't that how it happens? She wrapped her arms around me so tight that I felt there was absolutely no way I could get loose even though I pulled against her like the weight of gravity. Jackale pulled me into her crotch and I could feel her "w" grinding against my butt as she fondled my thang. It all felt so X-rated. In fact, it felt "XXX-rated" to me (Lol!). She covered my mouth with her other hand then started sucking on my earlobe as she verbally terrorized me. "See there lil' niggah, I told you I was gon' get you, didn't I? Now, I'm bout to drag yo lil' ass inside and pump on you and ain't nobody here to stop me

15

either." All I could think about was being tied down, gagged and...well, I didn't quite know what else, but at the time I didn't think I would enjoy it. At that moment, I broke loose from her grasp and the force of my pull flung me to the sidewalk face first and the gallon of milk busted open and spilled all over the ground. I didn't even care. I jumped up running without looking back.

I only lived six houses away and I was a fast runner so I got home immediately and ran inside huffing and puffing with a look of terror on my face. I didn't know whether I was more frightened by Jackale's latest attempt or explaining to my mother what happened to the milk. My mother looked at me like I was crazy and asked what had taken so long? Then she looked at me again as she saw that I was visibly shaken. "Well, where's the milk?" she asked. "What's the matter with you boy? Where's the milk I told you to get?"

I wasn't ready to answer any questions just yet. So, I offered her my very best eight- year-young response. "Uhhh. Huh?" That obviously wasn't the response she was looking for. "What do you mean, huh? Negro boy, where is the milk I told you to get? What took you so long to get back and why are you looking like that?" My sister came out from the back room as I stood there looking at my mother in silence. My sister instinctively seemed to know it all had something to do with Jackale. So she started the dialogue. "Was it Jackale?" I shook my head in agreement to her assumption. My mother looked me straight in my eyes. "Ok, tell me what just happened to you." I stumbled and mumbled through the event as my mom put on her shoes. I knew exactly what was about to happen and it wasn't gonna be good for Jackale.

Later, my mom went down to Thamont's house and told Jackale's mother what happened. Man, I heard she got the beaten of her life, got put on punishment AND she had to apologize to me! It was all so embarrassing. Needless to say, Jackale never said two words to me after that. She never even looked at me. I have to admit, it was a big difference. I really missed all that attention. But, I guess that's where my particular type of woman was cultivated. Since that time I've always preferred older women, with a perfect blend of assertiveness, initiative and aggression (like Jackale), softness and smooth feminine seduction (like Genise).

Growing up, Goin' Down.

You grow up pretty fast in the ghetto and it doesn't take long before your vernacular changes. I remember the very first time I almost went down on a girl. In the early 70's, I didn't know the name for it; they just called it "nasty." I was about nine years young and had this real fast girl in my class who was always telling boys to lick her pussy. You could tell she'd been around adults who'd taught her too much too soon. All the other little girls in my class would at least pretend to pull away when you pumped on them. But this little heafa had absolutely no scruples, which of course made her the most popular girl in the class. Actually, I was a little bit intimidated by her because I wasn't used to a little girl being so (sexually) liberated. She would actually FEEL on the boys, and let them pump on her from the front and back simultaneously. Now THAT was extremely disturbing to me. It was difficult watching her let virtually every boy fondle her. I guess even back then I needed to feel special and I refused to be just "one of the boys." But obviously, I was the only boy who felt that way.

...

[I remember she got me in big trouble because she wrote the letters p-u-s-s-y on my test paper. When the teacher saw it she immediately questioned me then called my mother. I was forced to play stupid because in the early 70's, upstanding parents would "tear-yo'-ass-out-the-frame" if they even thought you knew the definition of the word pussy. I remember my grandfather (who was the closest thing to Jesus because he was a religious man and a deacon...Lol!) and my mother interrogated me for a good hour attempting to make me disclose what pussy meant. "What does this word mean?! Tell us right now, what it is!" I was crying my ass off. "I don't know! I don't know!" The two of them even tried to make me pronounce it. "Sound it out! How do you say it?!" The whole thing was soooo embarrassing. I wasn't sophisticated enough to turn the tables and ask them the definition or how to pronounce it. Now, that would've stopped the show (Lol!). But, you live and learn. The funny thing about it was neither one of them ever actually said the word. I was just waiting, so I could drop dead from the shock of hearing my dear mother or "Grandpa Jesus" say the word pussy. Yeah, that would've either killed me or scarred me for life.

I must say, that nasty little heafa caused me a lot of trouble that day. In fact, I saw her at the dry cleaners several years ago. I was picking up some clothes one evening and she walked in. One thing about me is that I don't forget a face; it's sort of like a gift, especially when you consider I hadn't seen her in about 30 years. She was high than a muthafucka too! I could smell weed all on her. I called her by name and she looked at me like, "Niggah, who is you?" I told her where she grew up, the elementary school she attended and how she got a little boy in trouble one day many years ago. She turned redder than her eyes (and she was a brown sista too). She remembered, and actually started apologizing for some shit that happened over 30 years ago. We both laughed about it. Then she said, "Listen, I didn't grow up to be a bad girl." I told her she didn't have to qualify herself to me. But, I didn't believe her ass anyway. If she was like that at nine years young, I could only imagine what she'd become since then.]

...

One day she told me to lick her pussy. I thought about it for a second and I was like, "Bet!" She told me to do it right then. We were sitting way in the back of the class so I got up under the table and that little heafa actually pulled down her pants and her panties. I tried my very damnedest to reach her coochie, but because of the way the table was made, I couldn't. I was less than a half-inch from licking my first coochie at age nine. Remember, initially I said I almost went down.

Another little girl in the class saw my attempt and her eyes bugged out as she covered her wide-opened mouth with her hand. I placed my finger against my lips signaling for her to keep quiet and she obliged, after nudging the girl next to her. Looking back, I wish I had succeeded. I can't even imagine what I would've become if I had. It was probably for my own good that I didn't succeed, because I would've loved it (as I do now) and started licking every little girl who'd allow me to. Unfortunately, I didn't try it again until eight years later.

The Playa Chronicles

I was fortunate to have what most people considered a very pretty (older) sister, which automatically made me the little brother to all the older guys in my neighborhood who were interested in her. And, since pretty girls usually have pretty girlfriends, our house became a magnet for many of the older guys in my neighborhood. They hung out at our house and got cool with me to get in good with my sister and her girlfriends. For some reason, each of them felt it was his "civic duty" to school me on women.

"Listen up little playa, don't you EVER go for the two-for-one." I asked, "What's the two-for-one?" "That's when you give a girl some money for her pussy. Don't be no sucker little niggah! That bitch gettin' yo' dick AND yo' money and all you gettin' is her pussy. The shit you got between yo' legs is just as valuable as what she got between her legs and don't you believe nothin' different! I don't care how ugly you are or how small yo' dick is, that bitch gettin' SOMETHIN' out of it. You can believe that!" Then they would all give each other low-fives. That was in the mid 70's before high-fives became popular. Now, at age 10, I felt honored to have the big guys pass on "the secrets". I hung on to their every word and immediately made it my personal philosophy. I must have heard every derogatory slang term for women from those guys: bitch, trick, tramp, whoe, slut, tack-head, bucket-head, and boot-mouth. That was my orientation, but that was only the street perspective.

The big FO'

The in-home perspective was altogether different. You see, there were four men who greatly shaped and influenced my young life: my two grandfathers, my dad and my stepfather. My dad was a smooth city-slicker with a short man's complex, a compulsive gambler with a quick-temper who didn't take no shit from nobody, and I mean nobody. Any ass he couldn't kick, cut or stab...he shot. My mom has an entirely different view and early description of my dad, perhaps because of all the pain and stress he caused her. However, she's a Virgo and once you injure one of them, they rarely, if ever, forget or forgive you. But, I never let anybody (including and especially my mom) color how I viewed my dad. Even then, I knew to judge people according to my own experiences with them.

Unfortunately, besides dabbling in other mind-altering substances, my dad was also a heavy drinker. Alcoholism wasn't the name for it in the 70's. We just called it getting drunk and he got drunk a lot, and often-times when he came home he'd take it out on my mother. You just never know the awful affects domestic violence has on a young child. I can re-member being awakened many nights by my parent's arguments and en-suing fights. I remember my sister and me peeking out of the bedroom door to see the violence. I can recall it like it was yesterday.

My sister would really get involved. We never ran out to help until she gave the signal. I would just stand there in a total state of shock. But her cue of, "come on let's go" would snap me right into action. We were like Batman & Robin and since I was the youngest, I was Robin. Then, it was three on one. Even through his intoxication, once my dad realized his four- and seven-year-old children were trying to protect their mother, he would either leave or stop. And, if he didn't do one or the other, we'd leave and then it was off to grandma's house. But, all the while we were grabbing his legs and hitting him, I thought to myself: This is some real strange shit! I felt like I was betraying my father while trying to protect my mother. I never hated my dad; I loved him dearly. I just hated the violence he unleashed upon my mother.

Strange Love

The first time I ever saw a man cry
Was when I saw my daddy cry

And even though it made me cry,
I failed to grasp the reason why.

Because I never really cried
When he blackened mama's eyes.
It was hard to sleep through her screaming
As the abuse was applied

I couldn't tell you what was stranger:
My love for them,
His love for her,
Or her love for him

Strange love...deranged love...could somebody please explain love
That would make Tina stay with Ike?
Strange love...insane love...profane love
Objection overruled, with emotion to strike. Strike one! Strike two! Strike three...she's out!
Viewing such horror as a four-year-old child
Made me vow
Never to hit a woman...But in the here and now,

She hits me first
And what makes it worse?
She starts the shit, with the intent of getting hit
And has the nerve to grab her coat and purse?

Strange love...deranged love...
How can you maintain love that makes you cry?

21

Strange love...feigned love...disdained love
That hurts and makes you wanna say good-bye

Arguments...disappointments...disagreements...jealousy
Emotionally drained...feeling illegally detained
Infidelity! Niggah what?
You've been cheatin' all this time and just now tellin' me?

Naw, this ain't feelin' productive
And now I'm reluctant
Because of too many promises unkept

It's just too much drama, go on back home to yo' mama.
Fuck this shit! I should've BEEN don' left

Strange love...deranged love...but please don't blame love
If there's no smiles & laughter
Just know that ordained love...is not obtained love
But your main love...is self-contained love
And that same love... will leave you...happily ever after.

    I remember one Easter my dad took my sister and me to his girlfriend's house. Yeah that's right, the woman he was fuckin' 'round with. Now, that was some Ol' Gangster Mack shit. Only a real G-Mack would do some crazy shit like that! She was really attractive too and even at five years young, I could sense her sensual vibe which is probably at least one reason he liked her. She had this real sexy quality about herself that my mother did-n't have. She also had two children, a boy and a girl.

    My dad bought her daughter the exact same shoes he bought my sister for Easter (or vice-versa). I'll never forget those shoes: they were round-toe red patent-leather with a gold buckle. My dad tried to humor my sister and her daughter about the fact that they were wearing the same shoes. Her daughter was amused by it. But my sister was NOT buying any of that bullshit and I could tell she had an attitude. I mean, I knew my dad was doing some real renegade type shit, but I just flowed with it. Not my sister. She was strictly a mama's girl and I knew exactly what she was gonna do when she got home -- spill the beans to my mother!

...

[When my dad made his recent transition, this same woman attended his funeral. I knew who she was once my dad's cousins greeted her by name. Even after 40 years, she looked like herself. She made sure she spoke to me and seemed happy to do so. "Hey there, you may not remember me because you were probably too young, but I'm yo' daddy's friend, Shariann." I just played it off like I didn't know who she was especially since she'd already given me an alibi. I mean, what was I supposed to say? "Yeah I remember you. You were the woman my daddy was fuckin' 'round with when I was a child, right? I spoke very cordially to her. But my sister recognized her right away and unfortunately, but predictably, my sister let her ass have it when she tried to speak to her. I told you, my sister is strictly a mama's girl and she sure can carry a grudge.]

...

I can also recall my dad letting me hold his pistol one day as we were riding down the street. I was in the front passenger seat and as we came to a red light, he took out this huge pistol from under his seat and told me to hold it for him. He actually tucked it underneath the waist of my pants and everything. He got the greatest kick out of watching me hold it. When we got to the next red light, I was looking over at my dad when suddenly there was three loud knocks at the passenger side window. It scared the shit outta me to the point where I jumped and almost shot myself. You see, I had my finger on the trigger the whole time but thank GOD I didn't pull it, or I might not have "the balls" to tell you this story...quite literally.

When I turned around it was some rough, gangster-looking dude wearing a Boss-a-lini hat with his face up against the window. My dad reached over and rolled the window down, "Hey niggah, what's happnin'?" They started laughing and talked for a minute. I was just glad my dad knew him. As we drove off my dad took the gun from me and put it back under his seat. I distinctly remember him being just a little perturbed that I was startled by the knocks on the window. Or, maybe he realized it wasn't the smartest thing he could have done. In either case, I recall feeling kinda bad because he was irritated. I didn't spend a whole lot of time with my dad in my younger years but as you can see, some of the times I did spend with him were certainly memorable.

Now, my dad's father was a very religious, levelheaded well-to-do entrepreneur (yeah, they were total opposites). He owned and operated his own construction company and made six figures in the early 70's when it wasn't popular for middle class Moors (blacks). He had a nice big home with two Cadillacs and a work truck. He was the sole breadwinner, and had plenty of dough to make the bread (Lol!). His wife prepared three hot delicious meals seven days a week, kept his house in immaculate condition and didn't give him too much lip. They reminded me of June and Ward Cleaver on "Leave it to Beaver."

My grandfather had the final word on everything. He was a man's man. Instead of ruling by physical force like his son, he ruled emotionally with the bible and since his wife was a god-fearing woman it was a perfect situation for him. My granddad gave me my sense of morality as well as my early knowledge of GOD. If you talked to him for more than five minutes, GOD and/or the bible would find its way into the conversation. I often found it utterly amazing how he could segway from any topic of discussion to religion. He really showed me how to be a man. I don't ever recall my grandfather actually saying he loved me, but he never had to because he always expressed it through his actions. He raised me as if I were his very own son after my parents divorced. Initially, I thought it was because he felt compelled to do so since his only child abandoned his grandchildren. But, in recent years I discovered my grandfather abandoned my father just as my father abandoned my sister and me. Perhaps, my granddad raised my sister and me to compensate for his own negligence with his son, and possibly to sooth his own guilty complex. My grandfather recently transitioned to that higher dimension most people call heaven. I don't really miss him though because it feels like he's inside of ME for all eternity.

Heaven Is In Me

Where is heaven?

They say heaven is where GOD is

Well, GOD lives in me

So am I to believe that heaven is in me?

Spirits can't walk on streets of gold

And spirits can't wear long white robes

Wisdom's brought me to a place in time to know...

Heaven is in me

Love and laughter

Makes life wonderful and worth living

And the life after?

Is rest from a full life of giving.

No more fairy tales of pearly gates

My eternity is now, I don't have to wait

It's not impossible at all to contemplate...

Heaven is in me

Yeshua gave us the example of just how to live

To daily sacrifice your life for someone else

Living every day for RA and offering your very best

And your forever will take care of itself...

Heaven is in me

My mom's dad was a 33rd degree Mason, a very wise and reserved spiritual man. He was real mysterious, patient, kind and loving. Everyone loved, revered and respected him. He was slow to anger and quick to relinquish it once his point was made...and his point was always well-taken. He was the kind of person that a wild ferocious animal would withdraw itself from out of sheer reverence, and I found him humorous because I, along with everyone else who knew him, was hard-pressed to find something wrong about him. For all practical purposes, he was perfect. The strange thing was, with all that going for him, his wife was a mean, vindictive hellion. As a small child, I often wondered how the two of them came together. In his later years he became a very sickly man who literally had about 15 heart attacks before making his transition. Once he became ill and his wife refused to care for him, my mom took her father in and cared for him five years until his death.

I kinda saw my granddad as a push-over who couldn't handle his woman. I didn't like witnessing the way his wife back-talked and mistreated him as he maintained such a humble attitude. Many, many years after his death, his oldest brother told me my granddad (in his youth) took a straight razor and damn near split a Caucasian man in half, back in the South. For whatever reason the man kicked my granddad, and he cut him deep, hard and long from his navel all the way around to his spine. In fact, my great- uncle said my granddad had quite a reputation for carrying a straight razor and knowing how to use it. Even though the man lived, my granddad's family moved him up North to save his life. So, he wasn't perfect, but to me– he was close.

Perfection

Theoretically speaking, a man can never peak
Because, despite his philosophical, mental, or spiritual strengths
There's always an area where he's apparently weak.

It's widely known that we only utilize a fraction of our brain
And few are willing to profit, learn and grow from their intangible pains

Thus, everyday ought be a search for a challenge or situation
That will initiate positive change for the better good, and its relation.
Not necessarily just for one's self, but mostly for everyone else.
It's our human obligation.

We must continue the strive to modulate
And initiate the drive to propagate
Information that will germinate the seed, and instigate the need
To continually stimulate all that we are, can become, and breed

We should always attempt to graduate, onto higher levels of correction.
Reaching for, yet never grasping, that coveted possession of perfection.

Perfection...the real affection of true spirit beings
And the rare selection for those not attuned to spiritual things.

Perfection...chasing what can't be caught, learning what can't be taught...
buying what can't be bought.

Perfection...the highest height, the deepest depth, the widest width...
Perfection...akin to infinity and eternity...the most expensive gift

Perfection...the oldest married flirt to never commit adultery
Perfection...the most sought after virgin with flawless fidelity

Perfection...the vote for a candidate that can't be elected
Perfection...the circumference of a galactic-sized monument never to be erected

Perfection...the fulfilling of one's full potential leaving nothing behind
Perfection...an eternal maturation process of one's soul, heart & mind.

Perfection is not without origin, of course.
But, it can only be found in the DIVINE CREATORS.
THEY are perfection, for THEY are its source

My step-father is a militant intellectual who is Nat Turner, Malcolm X and Marcus Garvey all rolled into one, a real out-spoken, dogmatic type guy. He was always shouting, 'Black Power! Revolution!' He could adequately point out all the problems of the world as it relates to Moors (black people), but never offered or shared the solution. He's a non-religious man who was often seen as a radical fanatic with a hint of atheism. Or, at least he didn't endorse the God of the Holy Bible. Growing up, I listened to his every word (though I never let him know it) because he always spoke with such passion and conviction his rhetoric had to have some validity. I have to admit though, some of the shit he used to say was so amazingly off the beaten path. But, as I grew up I came to realize and discover some of his theories and ideas were extremely accurate.

Stay Black

This ain't no Black Power bullshit!
Just some Nubian excrement
A fecal matter, that, I must tell
Because my voice is Heaven sent.

Now I distain snow-game
As much as golf is a snow game
I wouldn't, even if Tiger would.
Hitting white balls real hard is alright with me
But snow plowing just ain't my thang.

Well, I don't want another "Rosewood."
So there'll be no "Jungle Fever"
O.J. and Colby didn't help the cause
Without question, they gon' always believe her.

A bunch of Oreos think it's all that.
And some see it as sweet revenge
For the plantation daze, fuck that!
We gonna clap-back
While true realest Niggaz just cringe.

My father, his dad, my mom's father and my step-dad-- four completely different men-- helped shape my personality, and somehow I retained all of their prominent attributes, while integrating them with my own. The four of them are an amalgamation of my very being, and each of them surface within my expression. They surface in my various styles of dress, in my conversation and even in my writing. I can be intellectual, spiritual, radical, philosophical, and ebonically out spoken, all in the same paragraph (Lol!). But most of all, the four of them, plus my own personality AND the street perspective made me a muthafucka to deal with as it related to women. My youthful personality was vastly different from my patriarchs. I was very shy and somewhat withdrawn, but very observant and because I'm a Pisces, extremely intuitive. I'm also very passionate and loving to the chosen one. But in the true Piscean spirit, whoa unto the person I deem unworthy, for there's no colder shoulder than my own.

At this young stage of my life, I had an extremely warped, demented view of the female gender. The bible describes a woman as the weaker vessel, depicts them as evil or trouble-causing and in many cases second-class citizens. Or shall I say, sub-human? It had to be right, right? Because if GOD said it then it must be true, and unfortunately back then I thought the bible was the actual words of GOD. I saw women in the same way my mom's mother used to describe children: "They should be seen and not heard." To me, nurses were subservient to doctors; teachers were subservient to principals, stenographers to judges, so forth and so on. You see, I grew up in the 70's. So in my personal experience, most teachers, nurses and stenographers were women; while most principals, doctors and judges were men. I'm very certain my granddad's rule over his wife, the wicked and disrespectful way my mom's mother treated her husband and my dad's frequent beat downs upon my mother all substantiated God's Word.

Dear Mama

...And, if all those elements weren't enough to distort my view of the female gender, my mother's rearing of me didn't help the cause. I was the only boy and the youngest child in my family. Also, my mom mentioned more than a few times in my youth that I was the result of a planned pregnancy (although she just recently told me otherwise...Lol! So, I really don't know which to believe because she's been known to change her story to benefit her point.)

...

[However, my mom's current claim of how I came to be is this: she went to the doctor to get relief from severe coughing that caused her to bleed from her throat. Upon examination, the doctor informed her she was pregnant. She felt that was pretty strange considering she wasn't there for a pregnancy test, nor had she requested one. She was absolutely appalled because her marriage was in shambles and having another child was not on her agenda (according to my mom, she was pregnant a total of 11 times. However, only my sister and I came to fruition). Well anyway, my mom informed my dad of the doctor's findings and felt it was senseless to continue taking birth control pills when she was already pregnant.

I was scheduled to be born two months before my actual earthday which meant the doctor's initial findings were absolutely incorrect! My mom WAS NOT pregnant on that particular doctor's visit and I was actually conceived after she stopped taking her birth control pills].

...

So planned pregnancy or not, I was a miracle child because I wasn't even supposed to be conceived, let alone born. To me, that's even better than being planned. It confirms I'm alive for a divine purpose and NOTHING will stop me from fulfilling my destiny. On top of that, I was a very sickly child and spent as much time in the hospital as I did at home until about age four because I developed two dis-eases in my infancy. Incidentally in my mid-thirties I discovered through personal research that both ailments were really adverse effects from vaccinations FORCED upon infants in the 1960's. I say forced because there was really no way to avoid the vaccinations. Supposedly, babies had to receive them before leaving the hospital. The strange thing about those vaccinations was that all of the (man-made) dis-eases they were also supposed to alleviate were already eradicated by that time: polio, small pox, etc. And, so many children who were immunized still caught the dis-eases the vaccinations were supposed to alleviate (chicken pox, mumps, etc.) So, what were/are the real reasons for these vaccinations??? Even today, why are hepatitis vaccinations given to infants? Hepatitis is primarily contracted through sexual contact and I don't know any infants involved in sexual intercourse, do you? So what's really going on???

Well, that's actually another book all together. But in brief, the vaccinations were actually inoculations especially forced upon melanin dominant (black) newborns mainly to fuck up their DNA, induce dis-eases, decrease their advanced supernatural/psychic abilities and retard their innate super intelligence...basically to injure the Indigo Children. You don't have to take my word for it. PLEASE do your own research.]

...

Anyway, long story short, I was the center of my family's attention because I was the only boy, the youngest child, allegedly the product of a planned pregnancy and sickly. So, I was reared to be self-centered and more than a few women have told me, I haven't changed very much in that regard (Lol!).

My parents divorced shortly after my fifth birthday. Thank GOD! Otherwise, they may have ended up killing each other. I mean, it was a real toxic atmosphere, but ironically it became even more toxic for me in the years after they divorced. Many times, young Moor (black) boys are made to suffer after their parents separate and divorce. Not just from the absence of their most authentic male role model--their father-- but, also because of the mental, emotional and physical abuse that's perpetrated against them by an ironic and least likely source...his mother.

Many Moor (black) boys have been viciously abused and victimized by psychologically damaging statements like: "You act jus' like yo' no good rotten ass daddy," or, "Yo' daddy ain't shit and you ain't gon' be shit either." Trust me, these kinds of verbal lashings can hurt, bruise, and scar far worse than extension cords or belts. Physical wounds often heal, but intangible (emotional) wounds can often last a lifetime. It's not even necessarily that the father is a no-good, no-account, rotten bastard at all. However, she (the supposed victim) sees him (the supposed abuser) in that way for personal reasons (hurt, pain, betrayal, abuse, jealousy) and transfers her toxic views and opinions right into her son's psyche; fully unaware that she's destroying his very self-esteem. And, even some of the corporal punishment viciously bestowed upon young Moor (black) boys by their mothers is far more excessive because, in some way, they remind them of the man who caused them pain...their father. So, while they are beating the hell out of little Jr., she's symbolically and simultaneously also beating the shit out of their abuser.

I'd have to say I was also a victim of such abuses and I witnessed it in so many other Moor (black) families. I'm certainly not insinuating that this scenario is the majority of the Moor (black) family's experience, but it was MY experience. I used to wonder where my mom's toxic statements derived from since she primarily raised me. How could she claim I was so much like my biological father when he wasn't around to impact or influence my personality and behavior? Logically, it was most probable I'd be more like her since she raised me, right?

But, what was worse than fighting the thriving inferiority complex she birthed in me (after my 11-year reign as the 'Prince of Planned Pregnancy') was my growing disregard and disrespect for women based on her abuses upon me. My mother, bless her heart, was probably doing the best she knew how to do under her circumstances in relation to raising me. Most people (and parents) usually do better if they know better. So, I'll just take for granted she didn't know any better. My dear mother didn't specialize in that motherly type of love. She was more of a tough love type of mom.

Maybe tough love was her mastermind plan to cultivate manhood within me since my biological father was unwilling to do his part.

My stepfather was present, but not very easy for me to embrace. Honestly speaking, whether he (and many other stepfathers) will readily admit, it's difficult for a man to fully embrace a male child that isn't his own, especially during the boy's adolescence. No matter what, that young boy is a constant reminder of his mother's 'ex' who predates him as her current love interest. This is perhaps a more subtle example of baby-DADDY drama and it's considered subtle ironically because the drama takes place vicariously in the absence of the baby's daddy. Therefore, when the young boy seeks attention from his mom, her current love interest sees it as her 'ex' jockeying for her attention. This view is very prevalent if the young boy challenges his stepfather in any way. It's viewed as a personal challenge from her 'ex,' especially if the young boy just so happens to look and act like his biological father. It's been said in life you get the mother best suited for you. Well, I don't know if that's true or not, but my mom's rearing of me helped to cultivate an already germinating seed of disregard and disrespect for the female gender.

Adolescence

I grew up in a 'glorified ghetto' (a lower middle-class neighborhood) where there were only a few things that captivated a young Moor (black) boy's mind: money, criminality, sports, respect and sex. Perhaps not in that order, but sex was the common denominator. Seemingly every single thought, word and deed of a young Moor (black) boy led back to one of the above mentioned. I remember getting up every morning with sex on my mind primarily because I was awakened by wet dreams. Changing my sheets every other day was just a normal occurrence. I was extremely dark during my adolescent years, and as you know melanin is pure energy. So my libido, imagination and anticipation for sex only rivaled breathing.

Homosexuality was a rare mention and a rare sight back then. I remember we used to dominate any boy that even possessed feminine traits or characteristics, let alone an admitted *sissy*. You see, in the ghetto there's a radar (gaydar) for that kind of shit because it's all about survival of the fittest and who's the toughest. The toughest got the most respect while punks, sissies, faggots, bitch-ass-niggaz, lames, snitches, police cadets, and suckers (or any combination of the listed with muthafucka added to the beginning or end of it) were constantly disrespected, and got their ass whooped regularly.

Gaze

Too many happy people
Too many different colors
What ever happened to all the sadness?
Before all this apparent gladness
Back when most people were the same shade of each other

Too much sunshine after a 40-day rain
Too many priests causing too much pain
Too many open minds
And narrow thinking is so hard to find

Too much new skool
What happened to all the ol' fools?
Playing by the old rules

Too many pots of gold at the end
Let's go back to silver, copper and tin
Too much female royalty
Too many partners of unity and loyalty

Too much of the self-same

Far too much 'bi-ing' and far too many trying

They say it's all-good, but I say they're all lying

Too much is unhidden and out in the open

What used to be forbidden is now for what many are hoping

Too many bends and curves

Whatever happened to playing it straight?

Do opposites still attract?

Or, is it being attacked

Let's change it all back

Before it's too late

Irony

I told my gay lover in the penitentiary

I was high on crack

The day after I murdered the prostitute

Who told my wife

I gave my little sister aids

When I got her pregnant

If you could fight real well, had a big family of brothers, were a thug, or a good athlete, you got respect back then. However, if you were categorized as any one of those, and just so happened to be a playa on top of that-- Shit!--then you were considered 'da man;' the most coveted title in the ghetto. There was a certain pressure to perform (sexually) at a young age; because if you weren't fuckin', you could've been labeled (as gay). The community (a.k.a. the hood) could spot an athlete a mile away. Guys with a lot of brothers were already well-known and a thug's reputation always preceded them. But, a playa wasn't always as easy to identify and because of that, most every Moor (black) boy in the hood either claimed to be a playa, tried to be a playa or at the very least claimed he was fuckin.' If by chance he really wasn't fuckin,' he did the next best thing...he lied. And, I was no exception. We must have sounded pretty stupid at 12 years young lying about our sex-capades. But we lied about our reality, as we lived in the fantasy of losing our virginity.

I actually had a couple of friends who really were fuckin' some of the hood rats and I'll admit, it was pretty tempting. But I've always had a need to feel special. Fuckin' a girl that half the neighborhood don' been in wasn't my idea of feeling special. So I passed on that. I dealt with some of the girls in my cousins' and friends' neighborhoods. But they were also community property, just in a different neighborhood. When I was about 14, a girl moved down the street from me who was kinda cute. But her most profound attraction to me was the fact that she was new to the area and hadn't yet been tainted by any of the neighborhood guys.

Her mom was a lot stricter on her than most of the other moms were on their daughters in my neighborhood. I saw her at the corner store one day and spit my game; she had to walk past my house to get to the store, so I saw her quite often. I initially started going to her house to visit because her mom wouldn't allow her to come to my house. Visiting at her house actually allowed me to get-in-good with her family. By doing that, I could gain their confidence and eventually they'd let her come down to my house. You had to do little shit like that back in the 70's.

Tam was a real nice girl and I came to like her over time. She was real quiet and seemed to have some difficulty expressing herself. But, even back then I was a great communicator. We spent so much time together she eventually came out of her shell...literally and figuratively. It really didn't matter, though. I was trying to 'hit them cakes.' I was so ready to lose my virginity (and stop lying to my peers) that I was willing to endure whatever I had to. That's about the time I discovered that expression and communication are more than just verbal; they can also be quite physical.

I thanked GOD above for at least two things growing up in my adolescence and as a teen--a house with an upstairs and the afternoon shift. Sometimes my mom worked from 3 p.m. to 11:30 pm, which gave me the flexibility to have my girl over in an anxiety-free environment. Even if my mom was home, as long as she was upstairs sleep, which was often the case, I could sneak my girlfriend into my bedroom and still operate pretty well.

We started out kind of slow...kissing and fondling each other. But, as the weeks progressed we went from kissing semi-clothed, to kissing fully nude. Now, she was a REAL virgin. Her pussy was tighter than the skin on a grape, and neither of us had licking and sucking in mind. By the time I was 14, going down on a girl carried one of the worst stigmas known to ghetto mankind. And since I wasn't about to be stigmatized, I just continued to do all that she allowed me to do. I used those opportunities to hone my foreplay skills. I got to the point where I knew just what to do to get the desired response. I studied her body and erogenous zones for about a year. It was like a graduate program at Foreplay University. And believe me; I received my Doctorate degree with honors.

We really liked each other and started goin' together. It was known throughout my neighborhood and all my boys knew about it too. I was even in good with her big ass brothers. It was about that time I found out that when you dry-grind long enough and strong enough...something comes out. I never did actually penetrate Tam and looking back I'm glad I didn't because it took a number of years before I acquired "dick control". If I had actually penetrated her, there's a good chance my first son would be 13 years older than he is today.

The Real Deal

I was in the 10th grade when my *career* actually began and I was more than ready. I had the street philosophy down pat, my game was strong, my rap was tight and my lies were as vivid as my fantastical reality. All I needed for my certification was an actual sexual encounter. The opportunity came on one of my many half-days of school. You see in the ghetto, a half-day was when you got the opportunity to do a lot of your devilment, treachery and skull-doggeries. Most parents never knew (and still don't) the half-day school schedule and most parents back then worked the day shift. So half-days were widely considered a free day for free play.

My first sexual encounter was with this real dark girl. I've always been most attracted to extremely melaninated (dark) women. My friends thought I was insane because back in the early 80's, light-skin was all that, especially if it was associated with 'good hair' and light-colored eyes. But I loved them dark (cute) girls and I didn't care what my friends thought about it.

I got acquainted with Lena in one of my classes. I was always the class clown and she found me to be very humorous. I could tell she was starting to dig me, but when a friend of hers told my best friend she dug me, it became official. Once I discovered that, I knew she was gonna be my first. As time went on I started talking shit to her about my sexual prowess to the point where she became real curious, and that's when we started planning the next half-day for our rendezvous.

On the special half-day, we caught the bus to my house, which was empty because sometimes my mom also worked the swing shift. I was talking big shit all the way there. I was so damn excited I didn't know what to do! The bus driver couldn't drive fast enough for me. Besides we had less than three hours to work with because my mom got home from work around 3:30 p.m., and I'd estimated us arriving to my house around 12:45 in the afternoon. Once we got to my house and inside my bedroom, I have to admit I was a little apprehensive because Lena really wasn't the kind of girl you wasted foreplay on. By the time I was 15, foreplay was for lames or strictly designated for your girlfriend, and neither was the case. I had to offer a different approach that I hadn't really contemplated, so I played it off like I was taking my time.

By the time I got the nerve to really make a move, it was after 3:00 p.m. and when I finally got her shirt off, (and she was extremely well-endowed) she was not impressed. "Well it took you long enough," she chimed in. "Well damn, did you want me to just come in, rip your clothes off and start fuckin'?" And she was like, "Yeah!" So I promised her next time it would go exactly that way.

The next half-day so happened to be seven days later, so our next encounter was already prearranged and I did exactly what she requested. As soon as she stepped across the threshold of my front door, I started unbuttoning her shirt. She loved it too. By the time we got to my bedroom, she was completely nude. I put on a rubber because I didn't want children or herpes (which was the a.i.d.s. of that era) and also because she lived near the projects and I heard that she was easy.

I slid in and it was official! I could tell she was experienced because it took a few strokes before she responded. For a second, I got nervous because I thought my dick wasn't sufficient enough for her. The worst stigma a guy could ever receive was the reputation of having a small dick. That was an ego-buster. But, after the third stroke, she responded as I had anticipated. Man! I couldn't believe it! I WAS REALLY FUCKIN'! I was grinning from ear to ear in my mind, but I had to stay focused because I didn't want her to suspect I was a virgin or inexperienced.

I kissed and sucked and played with her big titties for what seemed like forever. I must've *came* about five times in 10 minutes. I only had one condom so after I filled it up, I continued bare-meated. I quickly discovered that pussy can make you do shit you didn't intend on doing (but I had to finish what I started, right?). That's when I also discovered that pussy feels a zillion times better WITHOUT a condom. I also learned how to pull out. She never suspected that I was a virgin and she loved my passionate form of sexual expression. I made sure I gave her my best effort so she'd go back and tell all her friends. That was how you cultivated your reputation back then, which was also how you set up future encounters with other girls.

Yeah, my first encounter was very enlightening for me. However, I think I learned the most after our encounter was over. Lena wanted something called 'after play'. Now I wasn't familiar with that–you know, kissing, caressing, cuddling and sweet talk. Fuck that shit! My mind was strictly on how soon my mother was coming home and who I was gonna call and brag to after Lena left. Most of all, my mind was on how much I just wanted her to leave. You know that old saying: "You ain't got to go home but you gotta get the hell outta here?" I mean, it was really uncanny. I desired her so much before we started. But after my final release, I really didn't want to be bothered with her. Meanwhile she was all over me, and that's where the street philosophy rang true. My shit WAS just as valuable as hers because once we finished fuckin', she desired what she liked most--that intangible, inner-hidden part of me. Shit, I'd already gotten what I really wanted from her...the pussy.

At that moment, I (thought I) understood what the bible meant when it described a woman as the weaker vessel. I previously thought it was merely physical, but it was also emotional. I felt like I had the upper hand and with that, I could rule and enslave women in a manner unlike my patriarchs-with emotional manipulation. My personal version of pimpin' was birthed and from that day on I felt like it was my right of passage to run over, rule over and reign over the weaker vessel.

A Glimpse of Heaven

I was feelin' my own pimpin'. I dogged the shit out of all the 'unworthies' because it was fashionable to do. Besides, I was really just trying to 'get paid,' which I defined as girls paying your way, buying you stuff or giving you money. I wasn't pimpin' them sexually, because for me, the truest form of pimpin' was utilizing mental and emotional manipulation to extort money from women without having to engage sexually. All guys were trying to 'get paid,' but I was trying to do so whether I fucked them or not.

During that time I was involved in a high school organization, sponsored by a college fraternity, and we were invited to escort our sister organization to their national convention ball. Now, this wasn't a street affair. You see, young Moor (black) men in many cases live a quasi-faceted life. In the hood and on the streets, you're one person; in the church and around respectable people, you were another person. In school, depending on who you were around, you were someone else. With the girls, especially one-on-one, you were yet again different. At home, you're yourself. Then there was the preppy crowd, which was considered the complete opposite of the street crowd. With them, you had to be intellectual, have a sense of class and be very respectable. Acting ghetto was considered extremely crass. So, I had to put on my 'Carlton from the Fresh Prince of Bel-Air' persona for the weekend affair.

My 30 frat brothers and I were scheduled to attend a meet-and-greet on a particular Friday at a plush luxury hotel banquet hall. This function was designated for us to meet the young ladies we each were to escort to the ball the following Sunday. The young ladies' organization was sponsored by a sorority and it was the sorority's national convention. These young ladies hailed from all over the country: Cali, the Big Apple, Texas, Chi-town, etc. This was a young playa's dream. But, I couldn't use my street philosophy on these young ladies, at least not initially. A much softer, smoother, more sophisticated approach was needed. Remember, this was an extreme change of venue. So, that evening I got 'G'd up' to the max! That's a phrase we coined from GQ, the men's high-fashion maga-zine. If you were 'shaaarp' back in that time, you were described as 'G'd up' or 'G'd to the max!'

When we arrived, it was indeed heaven. I started mingling to see who the lucky young lady was going to be. The girls from L.A. were straight 'off the chain' (wild and loose). The girls from Texas were country than a muthafucka and the New York girls were quick-witted and fun as hell. We were scheduled to socialize from 6 p.m. to 11 p.m., and well into the night, I still hadn't made my choice (or hadn't been chosen). The expectation was to use all day Saturday to get acquainted with your pick.

I was entertaining a small group of six young ladies when I subtly no-ticed this darling little angel amongst them laughing at my humorous lines right on cue. [Maybe I should take this time to tell you about my sense of humor. I've always used humor to attract the opposite sex and make friends. It eases my anxieties; it fuels my personality and disguises my insecurities. But, when I'm really in my element and on my game, it's also quite seductive.] I mean, she was laughing so hard her eyes watered. She kept signaling me to stop so she could recompose herself before my next onslaught of humor. But, even at age 16, I was sophisticated enough to know when I had a fish on the line.

As I continued, I wondered how I failed to notice her beauty. I guess I was so self-absorbed in trying to be charming. She had this subtly-sensual -and-gorgeous 'vibe' going on. She was quiet, unassuming and extremely feminine. By the way, I simply love extreme femininity. When I started talking halfway serious, she asked me to say something else funny again, to which I replied, "Who am I, Bob Hope?" Her initials are A.L.E., so that's how I'll refer to her. The other young ladies knew my choice was made once A.L.E. and I mutually, exclusively and extensively gazed into each others eyes.

Her Eyes

It's in her eyes...innocence gazing at me
Watching her see, through the mind of girlish sensitivity.

It's in her eyes...looking at me
Daring to glare into the stare of pure sensuality.

It's in her eyes...
Sight unheard, talking so loud & saying so much
Caressing my heart with her warm, soft feminine touch.

It's in her eyes...
Peering at me visioning her
Bold yet coy,
Oh what a joy, to enjoy...being...in Joi.
Loving the chance to glance at her every moan and groan
I'm indebted & enriched by her "loan of pheromones".

It's in her eyes...

Looking at me, watching her...

Staring at me, gazing at her...

Glaring at me, visioning her...

Seeing me, peering at her viewing me...

It's in her eyes.

I saw the other young ladies file away one by one in my peripheral vision. I also noticed A.L.E. had somewhat of a British accent, which prompted me to ask her where she was from. She said Ontario. The only thing I love more than extreme femininity is when it's accompanied with an accent. She was a little spicy too, just the right balance of feminine and feisty. And despite her apparent soft-spokeness, A.L.E. appeared to be a leader amongst her peers and very well-respected by her mentors and chaperones. She wasn't like the girls from my hood; A.L.E. was different. She was soft and sweet and not afraid to reveal her inner feelings or speak her mind. She didn't play any games either. These were all traits and characteristics I liked in a young lady, but what made her even more intriguing was the fact that she wasn't from Detroit.

A.L.E. was definitely a take-charge kinda young lady and being that I was dogmatic, I hadn't realized how much I enjoyed that particular trait in a girl. It was so difficult for us to depart from each other by the end of the night because an authentic love connection had been made. I gave her my number before I left (this was before the cell phone age). She called me from her hotel room once I arrived home and we talked all night long. We were slated to meet the next day at noon. I wasn't gonna get much sleep, but I didn't care. We hung up about 5 a.m. and for the first time in my entire life, I woke up with a smile on my face. I was so happy to be alive on that day because there was something new to be alive for...love.

I spoke with my frat brothers about their experiences but none of them described anything close to what happened between A.L.E. and me. A few of them tried to 'hate' on me because they didn't make a love connection. They accused me of falling in love at first sight. Believe me, the thought crossed my mind, but then I rationalized, 'it's quite possible for two people

44

to hit it off right from the start. It's rare, but definitely possible.' Then they replied, "So what are you gonna do when she leaves on Sunday?" Now, that was a very valid question, but one I wasn't willing to entertain because we still had a day and a half left. So, I made the very most of it.

I couldn't wait to see A.L.E. the next day. That's the one thing about youth versus adulthood. When you're young, hot is so much hotter and cold is so much colder. All your emotions are heightened to maximum intensity. So, love or any derivative thereof is pure euphoria. I even told my mom about A.L.E. and my mom and I didn't even have that kind of relationship. She was so happy for me (and it was rare for us to display those kinds of emotions toward each other). My happiness even inspired her to buy me a new suit just for the ball. Perfect! Now, I was gonna be extra G'd up for the occasion.

When my mom dropped me off that Saturday I introduced A.L.E. to my mom and my mom's smile said it all. A.L.E. wore some 'daisy duke' shorts, except hers weren't blue jean cutoffs, and she was much more gorgeous than the night before. A.L.E. wasn't just sensual--she was flat out sexy! I really knew I was 'da man' when all my frat brothers started givin' me my props about her, including the guys who'd previously hated on me. It seemed like all the other couples were observing our interaction with each other. We went cruising through the mall and A.L.E. was turning virtually every man's head because she was fine as hell! And, away from that dimly -lit hall where we met the night before, her natural beauty stood out over the superficial beauty of most of her sorority sisters. But, even though she turned the heads of virtually every man everywhere we went, I was her sole focus of attention.

A.L.E. was all over me--holding my hand, hugging and squeezing me. Everybody around us could feel our energy. It felt like an out-of-body experience. Just before we left the mall, A.L.E. grabbed me, pushed me against the wall and deep tongue-kissed me. I was shocked, not to mention she could really kiss. Guys in the mall literally started cheering! All my frat brothers and her sorority sisters were so happy for us. We spent the entire day and most of that night together and it was more difficult for us to leave each other than the night before.

Once I got home, we talked on the phone until dawn but since the ball didn't start until 6 p.m., we were still able to get some sleep. Anxiety was starting to set in for both of us, because time was winding down for her to return home. It's funny how two days can feel like a lifetime. There was a mutual feeling between us that seemed like we'd known each other for eternity. We got along like we were made for each other and the short interval of time had absolutely nothing to do with it. We didn't have to hit it off as well as we did, or at all. Even as teenagers, we knew our romance, for lack of a better word, couldn't be taken for granted.

The night of the ball had to be the fastest five hours in the history of mankind. It seemed like the ball ended right after it started and just before it ended, our hearts became heavy. All the guys kept begging the D.J. for another slow dance song so the night wouldn't end, while the girls kept begging their chaperones for another 15 minutes. Our mentors and their chaperones were sort of getting their vibe on too, which actually worked out for our collective benefit. Plus, they all knew about our special little romance and seemed to respect it. I remember her crying on my shoulder. I'd never felt so melancholy in all my life. It felt like I was dying inside.

The D.J. was finally FORCED to stop the music at the request of hotel management. But, it was hell trying to drag 30 young Moor (black) men away from their Moorish female counterparts. We obviously weren't the only ones who made a connection; however, we were the most noted and celebrated couple. Everybody was exchanging numbers like they were going off to war. They started dragging us outta there around 11:00 p.m., but we finally ended up being officially kicked out around midnight. We went from the banquet hall to outside the banquet hall, from outside the banquet hall to the vestibule, from the vestibule to the hotel lobby, from the hotel lobby to the hotel parking lot.

Once I finally left, I had my mother rush me home so A.L.E. and I could talk on the phone. We were both so heartbroken; she cried all night long. I can still hear her painful wailing in my head almost 30 years later. I cried that night too and I'm not ashamed to admit it. Man, I was sick for about three weeks and my heart was so heavy that I couldn't eat and I didn't sleep. I can distinctly remember her telling me how she cried herself to sleep listening to Michael Jackson's "Human Nature" on the bus ride back home. And, to this very day, whenever I hear that song, it reminds me of her. She also described how her mentor literally cradled her while her sorority sisters consoled her as she cried.

We maintained a very close and special relationship through high school and college. We kept setting dates to come visit each other, but none ever came to fruition. We actually had one of the most successful long-distance relationships I've ever known. She wrote and called with the consistency of someone incarcerated. I had other girlfriends and she had boyfriends, but we were certain we'd get married after graduating from college, when the time was right. We'd already named our children and decided how many we'd have. We even made a pact that when and if we were ready to (sexually) explore with other people, we'd tell each other. I never did though; I just didn't have the heart. Maybe it was because I didn't love any of the girls I had sex with; I just liked fuckin' 'em. So, at any given time I had a minimum of two girlfriends, my main squeeze in Ontario and whomever I was fuckin' in Detroit.

Jack Pot!

After my 'real deal' encounter, I went on a hiatus from sex until my 12th -grade year. It was sorta ironic. I had waited so long and anxiously for my first sexual encounter and once I had it, I went celibate. Go figure. I grew up in church and had begun to really study the bible. I was being morally corrupted, so sex was considered a no-no. When I told my friends of my celibacy they refused to believe me; they just thought I was real eccentric especially since there were so many young ladies interested in me. The funny thing I noticed is that whenever I told a young lady I was celibate for religious reasons, they initially didn't believe me. But once they discovered I was serious, it made them desire me all the more. They took it like a personal challenge to see if they could knock the church-boy off his religious rocker. I actually had to stop telling 'em because it always backfired on me. But no matter how intense the battle, I always stayed the course and held them off--until I met my high school...teacher.

The Cats Meow.

I hear you purring
Pristine lil' cat with a Black panther's prowl
"Here Morris, time for din-din."
Tight lil' kitty's fiercer than a tiger
No lion...the lil' pussy is wild

I ain't scared of your scratches
Though I'm having a hissing fit from all your claws
Hunching my back for some whole new batches
Here lil' pussy, you don't have to lick yourself
I'll lick the kitty kat and gag on your fur balls
You smell that?
Yeah, that's me marking my territory
Looking for something I couldn't find
My mind...
'Cause I lost it when I found you

Feisty lil' feline playin' with her prey
I'll admit, I ain't trying to get away
Now, I've seen some bad ass cats in my day
But, 'chu 'bout the finest feline I've ever seen
And like a leopard, you know my G-spots
Lick it again lil' kitten, you got me hot!
'Nuff to make a Bob Cat like me wanna scream
She's pursuant as a relentless cougar
Panting like a hungry cheetah

Clawing all over me like Freddy Kruger treats an old school Elm-Streeter

I'm one bad battle-cat all scarred up
Scraped and scratched up for now
Seized and smitten by a tough lil' kitten
She's the sho' 'nuff cat's meow

My teacher was a heavily-melaninated girl with a grown woman's body. She was a size 12 with full lips and full hips. Sondra had smooth, even-tone dark skin but always wore a lot of foundation that was just a little lighter than her complexion (I guess they didn't have make-up for women that dark back then). She was obviously in denial about her true pant size because her jeans often hung an inch or so (tightly) below her crotch, like they were a size too small. She was always pulling her jeans up over her thunder-thighs, wide hips and big ass. On occasion, when she actually wore her true pant size, you could subtly see the outline of her pussy, accentuated by her full hips, which was DAMN sexy!

Sondra explained how she'd always dealt with older guys and condescended to talk to someone her age (in me). She said I was unique, cute and very sexy. In fact, she ascended my esteem by unveiling her fondness for dark men. I saw her last boyfriend, who was black as tar, and she always celebrated his melanin blushing whenever she saw him or talked about him. So from that day forward, I started sun-bathing and wearing colors that accentuated my dark complexion.

We were actually quite a sight to behold because I was a real small, short skinny teenager. But we were otherwise noted as a very popular couple because I always starred in the school play productions and I was the most popular radio personality on our school radio. Yeah I was well known, but Sondra was THE most popular girl at our high school. She lived with her grandmother because both of her parents were killed in the drug game...on the same day. They were a modern-day Bonnie and Clyde, gangsters who fell by the same swords they lived by. One day she told me the story of how she watched them murdered; they were shot to death. It was pretty sad, but she was a tough young lady, which is at least one reason why I liked her.

Sondra's aunt and uncle (who had real nice money) used to spoil the shit out of her as minimal compensation for the great loss of her parents. They kept her dressed in all the latest fashion and she wanted for absolutely nothing! Sondra really loved spending time with her aunt because she reminded her of her mom. Her aunt instantly fell in love with me when she met me because I was a cute, clean-cut, smart young man who was a far cry from the criminal element her family hoped she'd avoid. I guess they knew it was in her blood. Sondra didn't particularly like living with her grandmother, who was ultra-strict in trying to keep her from following in her mother's footsteps. Her grandmother was very old-fashioned and strong-willed. Sondra often appeared sad and sometimes even depressed, but that's where my daily visits always seemed to brighten her day.

Sondra was kinda rowdy and did her 'thug-thizzle,' and I heard she could really whoop some ass too, which is probably why so many girls were afraid of her. It was alleged that she had underworld ties through her parents (connections) and could get a guy fucked-up...or worse...if she really wanted to. That's probably why all the guys respected her. Her popularity intrigued me, but her sensuality attracted me.

We rode the bus to school together for months before ever talking to each other. We just exchanged looks. I guess we were both attracted by our preppy styles of dress. I'd been working at Wendy's since ninth grade and spent virtually every dime I made on the latest fashions in my own unique style. Sondra ran for homecoming queen in our senior year and as we filled our school auditorium (1400 seats), she RAPPED her home coming speech! Now, this was in 1983 when rap was hitting real hard. The entire auditorium went absolutely berserk! I was sitting with one of my frat brothers in utter shock. Man, she had a lot of heart! She had everybody so hyped they wouldn't even allow her to finish and she was probably crowned homecoming queen based upon that alone. That's when I knew she was gonna be my woman. I told my frat brother of my intentions (with his hating ass). "Man you can't pull her, she's the most popular girl in school!" he replied. (Now, that was some ol' punk-ass shit that really irritated me.) "So what does that mean, niggah do you know who I am? Like I said, she's gon' be my woman."

I started talking with her on our long bus rides to and from school. We were attending a high school outside of our district and we both used other family members' addresses to attend the school. After a couple of weeks of intense 'acquaintancing' we decided to hook-up on a half-day. We stayed about a mile away from each other which was awfully convenient. When she came over she got right to it; man she was aggressive! We didn't have sex but she was so explicit in everything she did, it sure felt like it. I could immediately tell Sondra was sexually advanced for her age, as if guys more advanced than her had schooled her very well. Sondra was the first girl to lick and suck my whole face when she kissed me. Now that was some brand new shit right there! We were both 17 and she wasn't necessarily religious, so it wasn't long before my celibacy armor started to crack.

I came to enjoy Sondra's possessiveness. There were a lot of young ladies at our high school who liked me but she made damn sure it only remained a desire for them. She didn't take no shit regarding that. She loved her some me! Sondra used to damn near beg me for sex...between her consistent rape attempts (I guess I kinda knew how it felt to be a woman. She was humorously intrigued and utterly amazed when I refused her for religious reasons. The way she used to claw all over me when we were alone! Youd've thought I was the woman and she was the man.) Sondra introduced me to quite a few new things. Oftentimes when we had sex, she'd have me close my eyes while she inserted my toes into her wet vagina. I don't know what it was about that, but that shit felt so good. She was also the first to suck my dick. In fact, to this very day I can truly say she's the main reason for my disinterest in receiving head. Not because it wasn't good, she just did it too much and too long which made me impervious to it. Sometimes we'd skip school and go to one of her friend's house (where other couples were skipping). She'd ask if we could use their bathroom and would tell me to stand on the toilet so she could suck my dick. In that regard Sondra was a nympho, but I really enjoyed her because she was courageously kinky. Whenever she sucked my dick at my house, she'd tell me to turn around then she'd spread my cheeks and lick my ass with fervor. She loved putting her tongue in my ass, but perhaps enjoyed my dramatic response even more. I'd turn around from front to back every two or three minutes because that was about as long as I could stand either position before it became unbearable. I came so often back then, it's a wonder I have anything left today. I used to hear guys always talk about how they wanted head so much. My desire was just the opposite because that's all Sondra wanted to do. That's when I discovered how emotionally bonding oral sex could be. She was also the first one to let me fuck her in the ass. But it was just alright; it would've been better if she had enjoyed it. She just wanted to honor my request.

But most notably, she was the first woman I went down on. In the early 80's we called it 'eating-out' and amongst guys, it was an absolute taboo! You'd have to move to China if the brothas ever found out you ate pussy, at least in my circles. It was the worst stigma a guy could have after having herpes or having a small dick, if it was discovered. If women found out you ate pussy, they'd ostracize you and brand you as a nasty muthafucka. But undercover and in secret, some of those same women and many others would definitely utilize your services. But since I had one hell of an oral fixation, and was aroused by the prospect of maintaining my secret desire of doing something so taboo, I was soooo anxious to try it...until I actually did. It took some getting used to--the aroma of her pussy and taste of her vaginal juices. Plus, I didn't really know what the hell I was doing, but she seemed satisfied. I think it was also an ego thing for both of us. Not only did we enjoy the physical side of oral sex, in our estimation, it was the egotistical and psychological gratification of having someone do something so totally antithetical to their cultural beliefs and watching them enjoy it. I mean, we always heard about Caucasian guys eating pussy and Caucasian girls sucking dick. But we considered that normal...for them! As far as we knew they originated it, but not in our sphere, at least not at that age. It was totally taboo for Moorish (black) girls to suck dick. That was the worst stigma a girl could have after having herpes and having the reputation of allowing guys to run trains on them. So we both benefited from and were fully-vested in each other's kink, because we enjoyed engaging in the very taboos we spoke against but held secret. Sondra considered herself a 'pimp-et', which was such a turn-on for me. I love confident women. The first time I ate her out she was lying in her bed talking to her girlfriend on the phone. She had one hand behind her head, relaxing, while she used her other hand to maneuver my head and stroke my face, as she held the receiver between her cheek and shoulder. Now, that shit was real sexy! You see, that's something a 'pimp-et' would do. Then she had the nerve to prop her feet up on my back...which made me cum. Sometimes she'd sit on her couch (naked from the waist down), spread her legs wide open and prop them up on the cocktail table. Then, she'd have me position myself between her legs as I licked her vaginal lips and eased my tongue in and out of her pussy like a dick. She'd lean her head back against the couch and roll it slowly from side to side, then raise her head and look down at me with a snicker admiring her pimpology. Back then, I wasn't aware of flicking my tongue against the clit, or licking that area between the pussy and the anus. I was just starting out and hadn't yet mastered the art and science of eating pussy. All I could do was emulate the shit I saw on porno films. Sometimes Sondra would hold my ears to guide my movements which used to remind me of how a man grips the back of a woman's head while she's going down on him. As she looked down at me, I could tell she relished her (apparent) position of dominance over my (apparent) position of subservience and it felt sexy for both of us. I'm more than sure she told her close girlfriends that she'd turned me out on eating her pussy. They always used to talk about how turning niggaz out on eating pussy made them pimp-ets (just like we men do). That's probably why her close friends always looked at me like, "Yeah niggah, we know what our girl has you doin' behind closed doors." Their looks always made me feel a little uncomfortable but as long as it never got out, I was cool. To this very day, I love going down on a confident woman in control (especially if she's older than me).

Sondra and I spent a LOT of time together our senior year...24-seven. We 'kicked it' until a few weeks after we started college. When I saw all that brand new pussy, real adult women of all nationalities and creeds? That was playa overload! I remember when she and I walked into our first college class together. This fine-ass woman was staring at me right as we walked thru the door. My radar picked up her 'vibe' and I just knew I was gonna 'get with' her. I could feel it in my spirit. It was kinda strange. I just kept meditating on thoughts of fuckin' her and a few weeks later we became an item. I immediately had to devise a way to get rid of Sondra. She had served her purpose and taught me what I needed to learn. Since, I no longer had use for her I created an argument which caused our break up and I never, ever looked back. Yeah, I know. I was terrible.

Dick Control

When I was 19, my high school buddy's ex-girlfriend moved into my neighborhood. I thought it was odd, considering by 1985, my neighborhood was more the place you moved away from. But, she was out on her own trying to be an adult sharing an apartment with another girl we went to high school with. This all occurred during a very trying time in my young life when my best friend was gunned-down. Murders and killings are daily accentuated in the Detroit news media, almost to the point of desensitization, and it only seems to become reality when it involves someone you know.

One day, I saw her at the corner store and asked what she was doing in my hood. I told her I lived right down the street from the store and she seemed both surprised and a little excited, probably because I was a familiar face in her new neighborhood. She promised to visit me sometime. I really didn't think too much of it (or her) partially because my mind was so focused upon my best friend's murder. Also, because she wasn't particularly attractive to me and had a funny shape. She was small and petite (as I prefer), but she had a high ass. You know, her butt sat damn near up on her neck (Lol!). Back in high school we shared several classes together, so I knew her to have a very obnoxiously extroverted personality. I perceived that her big personality was an attempt to compensate for her looks, or lack there of. It was pretty plain (for me) to see she was aware of her own shortcomings.

54

My buddy and her, along with Sondra and I used to double-date quite a bit back in high school. The most notable thing I remembered about them is how my buddy used to beat the shit outta her. I mean, you would've thought they were Ike and Tina. Curt was a pretty big guy with a jealous heart, but he was cool as hell and so fun to be around, the life-of-the-party type. He was valedictorian and one of the most popular guys in the junior class. He was a year behind us. But, he had one hell of a temper when it came to guys messing with his woman. He didn't play that shit! The crazy thing about it was how she seemed to enjoy pissing him off and making him jealous. She even seemed to relish the ass whoopings and most of the time Sondra and I, literally, had to pull Curt off of her. I used to get so angry watching her manipulate him into action, and then I felt sorry for her crazy ass when he jumped on her.

So, I knew I didn't have any interest in her, especially since she was my buddy's ex-girlfriend. You know how there's some things you just don't do because it's considered tacky? Besides, I was practicing celibacy for religious reasons and I certainly wasn't about to fall into sin with a 'bugar-wolf.'

One day she stopped by my house just as she promised and I was a little caught off guard because I'd forgotten all about it. It was the day after my best friend's funeral and I was so disinterested in her and what she was talking about. We stayed out on my porch, because I didn't really want my family to see her. Or, GOD forbid have them thinking I was associated with her! In fact I have to admit, I was just a little self-conscious about talking to her in public. As far as I was concerned she was a "bugar-wolf." You know, her momma was a bugar and her daddy was a wolf. In other words...she was ugly! But, she really seemed authentically sympathetic toward my loss and made me smile and laugh. Her genuine concern and attempts to console me kinda endeared her to me. I really appreciated all her kindness, because I was really messed up over my best friend's murder. She stayed over for a nice little while, until her face became cute, something like a "pretty monster (PM)."

In the short length of time she visited, I could tell she'd begun to like me. I mean, it wasn't like we'd just met. We were already pretty well-acquainted from high school and for all I know, she may have even liked me back then. But, dating my buddy (Ike Turner) and the threat of Sondra whoopin' her ass probably deterred her even if she did. I thought to myself...she ain't gotta chance in hell to get with me. So, her apparent lil' crush on me was real cute and innocent as far as I was concerned. She ended her visit by offering me an invitation to her apartment. I didn't give her a definite answer, but I knew she wouldn't let me forget the offer.

Like most 19 year olds, I was having a lot of friction at home with my parents because it was time for me to move out. It was just too many adults in one house and during that time, my mother's favorite daily rendering was, "If you don't like what's goin' on here, then get the fuck out!" Yep, she gave me the ol' if-then. I mean, a person can only hear so much of that shit until he's driven to respond. Well, Pretty Monster's lair was to be my new getaway. Yeah, I was looking to use her, but she didn't know it.

The first time I visited PM, her roommate wasn't there and she was all over me. I couldn't believe it! I literally had to (forcibly) push her off me. I just wasn't feeling her like that. She was ugly and I had a reputation to maintain. Besides that, I was saved and trying to live right. Plus, she was my buddy's ex-girl. Even though I hadn't seen him since high school, and probably wasn't going to, I still didn't want it to somehow get back to him. I actually told her I would leave and never come back if she didn't stop trying to molest me. She seemed really perplexed because she couldn't understand why I wasn't succumbing to her advances. When I told her I was saved and trying to live right, her facial expression said it all. She was in complete awe and a certain respect factor was established from that day forward. She realized I was unlike any other guy she'd ever dealt with and I saw the challenge in her eyes to eventually fuck me into submission. I started visiting her on a semi-consistent basis whenever my mom got on my damn nerves.

Honestly speaking, no matter how ugly a woman is if she continues offering the pussy, along with all the corresponding attention, the male ego usually breaks down. Mine did. Plus, I was so arrogant as to think I'd give Pretty Monster a pleasure and thrill she wouldn't ordinarily receive because I was 'the shit!' She was on me so tough one night and I was fighting it so hard, when I finally let her get into my pants you would've thought she'd just broken into Fort Knox. But, I didn't give in without a fight. I teased the shit out of her by rubbing my dickhead up against her clit and between her pussy lips. She was so hot and frustrated she literally snatched my pants off and ran in her room. Now, you know I couldn't just stay in her living room with no pants on with the chance of her roommate walking in at anytime. So, I was forced to go into her bedroom to at least get my pants.

When I got in her bedroom she slammed the door like a naked prison guard. She initially tried to give me some head, but as I mentioned earlier, I was all but immune to that so I stopped her, which confused her even further. Then she sat me on the edge of her bed and straddled me, but when she locked her legs behind me, that was all she wrote.

You know it's funny, before that moment I'd been celibate for months and my previous sexual prowess had been somewhat intermediate. But I surprised myself that night. As she was humping on me like a rabbit, I instinctively instructed her in my sexiest Barry White voice, "Uh-uhh honey...slow that shit down! You ain't going to a fire!" I told her to wrap her arms around my neck and I gripped her ass with both hands, pulled her so close to me, and she held me so tight you couldn't slide a sheet of paper between us. Then I eased her as far down upon my hard-ass dick as she could go, and I began slow-grinding inside of her like a Jamaican video dancer (Lol!). I shocked myself because I'd never even tried that position before. Prior to that, most of what I'd experienced was missionary style and a little bit of doggie style.

I was witnessing my own sexual transformation before my very own eyes. I even started talking shit in her ear: "You like that baby? How's that feel to you? Is that alright, darlin'?" And every time she sped up the rhythm (which was quite often), I whispered, "Uh-uhh...slow it back down." All this drove her absolutely crazy!!! She was moaning and groaning for real! Even back then, I'd heard that women sometimes faked it (like that could ever happen to me). But her moans and groans were authentically coming from out of the very depths of her soul. Then, I remembered that her ex-boyfriend (my buddy) was a real big guy. So, I considered the fact that he might've had a bigger dick, so I gave her my best effort, which really kicked my ego into full gear.

Prior to that time, the longest I'd ever gone before cummin' was 20 to 25 minutes. But this time was much, much different. Since I was so far up in her, and controlling the rhythm and because my arrogance dictated that I was doing Pretty Monster a favor. I slow-grinded her with a long stroke for over an hour. And trust me, I was watching the clock. That may not seem like a long time to y'all, but at age 19, it was to me. I was so damn happy about my new found 'dick control' that when she started crying from ecstasy, I gently spanked her ass and told her to shut up and stay in rhythm. I grabbed a handful of hair, pulled her head back and smacked her face. Not hard, just a few taps because I was caught up in the moment and she loved it! Then, I inserted my middle finger in her mouth to see if she would suck on it like a dick. And she did.

All of this was absolutely brand-spanking new to me. Fellas is it me, or do ugly women have some of the best pussy? I guess that's one of nature's ways of compensating for their looks, or lack thereof (Lol!). I finally worked up to a climax, pulled out and came after an hour or so. I didn't really know what to do after my stellar performance, so I put my clothes on and left. I couldn't believe I'd had the best sex of my life (up to that point) with a 'bugar-wolf.' On the walk home, I dealt with the guilt of sinning. But, I also had a desperate need to tell somebody how long I had lasted! And, this time, I'd be telling the truth. It wasn't until the next morning that I realized my back was all scratched up from P.M. clawing me, but I considered it a badge of honor.

After a few months, P.M. and I actually started goin' together. She was the first woman to do a lot of things to me, for me and with me. For instance, she was the first woman I ever took a bath with, the first woman I had multi-positional sex with and the first woman I spent the entire night with. It got to the point where I actually went out in public with her and even brought her around my family. I guess I was still convinced I was doing her a service by just being with her. Most importantly, she was the first woman to buy me. It's called being kept and being a kept man is fun, so long as there are no strings attached. However, I quickly discovered that insecure women often attempt to compensate for their (perceived) self-lack. She bought my college textbooks, which were expensive. She always bought me lunch or dinner and gave me pocket money. I remember being at the mall and seeing this bad-ass (expensive) blazer. She asked me if I really liked it and I knew right then she was gonna end up buying it for me.

But, there's a great lesson learned from being bought...there's usually some strings attached...usually the more expensive the gifts the more strings that are attached. I also discovered that insecure women often have more issues than normal. We started arguing a lot and with great intensity, and when we argued, I went home. But, I quickly returned to her apartment whenever I argued with my parents. I felt like a tennis ball at the French Open (Lol!).

PM simply loved arguing, fussing and fighting with me. It was unbelievable! She just didn't stop until I was up 'in her grill.' She'd drive me to the point where I was just about ready to smack the shit out of her. Then I started realizing why her ex used to whoop her ass all the time. She talked too damned much! PM often said those beard-yanking phrases which had the tendency to piss off guys. Then, once she discovered I wasn't the type to mishandle women, she only got worse.

I remember her reading me the riot act while arguing one evening. She named off all the shit she'd ever bought me, and it was a well-rehearsed list too. I was so fuckin' mad! I guess I hadn't realized how much shit she'd done for me and bought me. But truthfully, I was in so deep I couldn't say a word. It was a revelation I'll never forget. I hated that feeling of being played and felt she'd planned the whole scenario from the very beginning. But, the weaker vessel couldn't be that calculating, right? It was all merely coincidental, right? So, of course, I was ready to vanquish Pretty Monster back to her lair. But, I discovered once you regularly spend the night with a woman you've shared deep intimacies with, no matter how hideous she is, it's hard as hell to sleep in your own bed by yourself, especially at yo' mama's house. Her bed was calling me, sho' 'nuff. I mean, I was so hooked! It seemed like she planned that shit too. But, I just knew a mere woman couldn't accomplish that, not upon the stronger vessel.

I kept going back to P.M. but the arguments became worse and more intense. Also, the more I responded to her madness, the more out of control I became. Until one day she said the wrong thing. She criticized my sexual performance. Now keep in mind, I'd gone from fucking her for an hour on a regular basis, to becoming a 20-minute brotha. At age 19, I didn't know that mercy-fucking is different from infatuation-fucking. I also didn't know, in relation to my sexual performance, I had to maintain what I started. I had no intentions of falling for Pretty Monster; I was just doing her a favor, right? But in reality, she'd manipulated me in every possible way, or at least I allowed her to manipulate me because in the game of love there really are NO victims.

So one night, as too often had become the case, just as she was about to cum, I withdrew and came first...and she exploded! She called me everything but a child of GOD. "Muthafucka! God-damn-it! What's wrong with you, you can't fuck? He was at least good for that! (referring to Curt)." [Note to all female readers: NEVER, EVER criticize a Moor (black) man's sexual expression. I can't speak for any other nationality of men, but many Moor (black) men's egos are directly tied to their penis, and thus, their sexual performance. Yeah, I know it's an extremely debased masculine mentality (which probably derived from the nefarious "willie lynch" system), but I guess it is what it is.]

Anyway, before either of us knew it, I'd tossed her out of the bed to the floor, jumped on top of her, smacked her three times and spit in her face. I was shocked and frightened as it reminded me of the abuse I'd witnessed as a child. I officially knew right then we had a toxic relationship and it was only a matter of time before it had to end. P.M. cried when it all happened, but seemed to relish it all the same. After that incident, I began carefully monitoring my own emotions, especially during our arguments because I never wanted to lose control and initiate mishandling a woman ever again.

From that time on, I also began psycho-analyzing P.M., during which time she told me she never cultivated a relationship with her biological father. And as a young psychologist (Lol!), I came to discover and understand young women with little or no relationship with their biological fathers have an increased propensity for more intense issues and/or increased issues as adult women. In fact, promiscuity in women can often be traced back to poor relationships, or lack thereof, with biological fathers. Unfortunately, many such women spend portions of their lives subconsciously searching for fatherly attributes in men they consciously refuse to offer daughter-like submission to.

The Nerve of Some Monsters

By this time, I was spending about a week at P.M.'s apartment before going home for more clothes and to (physically) check in with my mother. One day mom gave me the ultimatum I'd been long anticipating. She told me I had to live in one place or the other because it was disrespectful to do otherwise while living in her house. But, I couldn't just move in with P.M. although technically I already had, to the point where my squatting annoyed the shit out of her roommate. Yeah, I felt bad about it, but so what. It was like the three of us lived together. Her roommate was pretty cool about it much of the time, but when P.M. and I argued I could tell she wanted me to leave.

Now, P.M.'s roommate was also a "bugar-wolf," but oooh, her body was bangin'! And yes, I thought about fucking her and probably could've. But she had the worst breath ever known to mankind. Her breath smelled like the crack of "Kunta Kente's" ass after a long, hard day's work. She must've chewed ass-flavored gum or something (Lol!). Even back then I was a stickler for excellent hygiene, so with her having dragon's breath, it was a wrap!

We'd been together about eight months when P.M. suddenly started getting home from work a little later each week. I didn't really ponder it until one evening as we were napping together; I dreamed she was fuckin' around on me. I was so arrogant and refused to believe that could possibly be the case. You know, with me being "the shit" and her being a "bugar-wolf" and all. As far as I was concerned I was giving her the thrill of a lifetime. But then, I started getting those subtle hints.

I used to catch the bus to her job and ride (the bus) home with her a few days a week. She was a waitress at a real nice restaurant. In fact, she always kept waitress jobs at four-star restaurants, and since she ate for free and I was her boyfriend, I got free eats! Remember, she had a real extroverted personality, so she knew everybody and was befriended by all her co-workers, most of which were fine-ass women who simply loved me to death (which was another reason I picked her up). For some reason, they thought we made the cutest couple. Also, I was always well-liked by the chefs of the restaurants where she worked because I had a tremendous appetite (especially for a little guy) and was so ultra-passionate about eating. So, I was by no means being a gentleman by meeting her at work. Yes, I had ulterior motives: she was my dinner meal-ticket and believe me, the food was delicious!

She started telling me I didn't have to meet her at the job or ride the bus home with her. I thought it was strange, but it really became a red flag when she started getting home a little later than usual. Then, sometimes her home phone would ring and if I answered, the caller would hang up. I used to catch her in the back room talking real low on the phone. One night, she came home a little later from work with a different scent on her. It was a masculine scent, not cologne, but a semi-musky-outdoorsy-with-a-hint-of-cigarette-and-light-alcohol scent. I smelled it when she walked in and discovered it was concentrated on the back of her neck.

I was pissed off but refused to reveal it because I had too much pride. Plus, we were on the brink of breaking up anyway. But then, my ego started taunting me. "Now, how you gon' let this ugly-ass bitch play you like that?" I tried not to question her, but my ego wouldn't let me. "Don't you wanna know what he looks like...if he's got a car (since you don't have one) or, most importantly, if he fucked her?

I learned some very valuable lessons during this phase of my life. In regards to infidelity, a woman wants to know, "Do you love her?" But, men wanna know, "Did you fuck him?" It's a very natural thing and damn it, I wanted to know! (Lol!) But more importantly, even to this day, I just can't stand being played, lied to, cheated on, toyed with, manipulated or allowing people to think they've gotten away with something (that really burns my anal canal). So, I interrogated the shit out of her until she told me what I wanted to know. She rather enjoyed it too, which made me even madder because I wasn't supposed to be jealous over a damn "bugar-wolf".

She told me he was a bus driver, several years older than us and lived with his girlfriend and children. Now, she claimed they hadn't fucked but admitted to kissing him (which was all the same to me). But, I actually felt better knowing, although I was just a college student, I at least had great promise. This guy was a bus driver for GOD'S sake, and that WAS his promise. Then she said he was a Vietnam Vet. So not only was he older than us, he was old as hell (Lol!). I figured he wasn't gonna leave his girlfriend and children for P.M. But, I knew he was at least interested in fuckin' her, which I definitely didn't want because she was MY pussy.

So, I continued reminding her that all he wanted to do was fuck her. But, to a woman with low self esteem, that was the whole point. I nicknamed him Rambo Kramden. I called him Rambo because he made it out of Vietnam and Kramden because Ralph Kramden was the main character on the Honeymooners, a bus driver going nowhere fast. We both thought that was hilarious! She was just happy receiving attention from another man. I was like "Fuck it!" We were breaking up anyway so I just went home. But, it was hard as hell sleeping alone, especially when you're used to having some kind of sexual act performed every night, and a warm, naked woman lying next to you. Even if she was ugly, she was gorgeous in the dark (Lol!). The only thing I kept thinking about was the notion of another man in my pussy. That was tearing me up inside!

We continued on and I thought their little fling had faded...until New Year's Eve night. I was under the assumption that we'd bring in the New Year together like we had before. Yet, I had this funny feeling (call it intuition) that we weren't. I was at her apartment while her roommate prepared to go out partying. I figured we'd just chill by ourselves for the night. However, shortly after her roommate left around 10:15 pm, she asked me to leave because she was about to have company. My heart sunk to my drawers. I was in shock! I couldn't believe she was about to break our tradition and make me walk home in the cold and snow so close to midnight.

In Detroit, there's a New Year's Eve tradition of shooting at midnight which, by the way, is taken very seriously. On this particular New Year's Eve night, they started shooting at 10 p.m., which wasn't uncommon. I just couldn't believe she was gonna send me home dodging bullets. Wow! Un-fuckin-believable! Another great lesson I learned during this phase of my life was: Don't ask women questions you don't really wanna know the answers to. I made the drastic mistake of asking if she was putting me out for Rambo Kramden to come over. Unfortunately her answer was yes. I walked home in the cold, hurt and mad than a muthafucka. I mean, I was hot!

My parents always partied on New Year's Eve, so they were already gone when I arrived home. I called P.M. a few times in my feeble attempt to 'cock-block.' She kept saying she'd call me back, but never did, so I kept calling her back. Then, she stopped answering the phone, which told me he'd arrived. I was so mad! She didn't even call me at midnight to wish me a Happy New Year!

It was all about the pussy and my ego was whooping my ass. "Now, you know he's over there getting yo' pussy, right?" I was trying my best to man up and silence my ego. "Shut-up ego, she was ugly anyway and well beneath my standard. Plus, we were just 'bout to break up anyway. There are a million gorgeous and attractive women out there." "Yeah, yeah, whatever you say man. He's fucking her, though! He's fucking her! Face it bruh...he's fucking her!" It was ringing in my head like a police siren. And, my imagination was playing it over and over again in my mind like the only film at a dollar show. I felt like going to her apartment to quench my curiosity. It was about 12:20 am (but the shooting doesn't stop till after 1 am).

I thought to myself "It would make me a real lame-ass, sucka-type stalker to risk my life and go spying on her to satisfy my curiosity." I felt like a broken-hearted, weak ass little punk trying to rationalize with my ego. "Shut-up ego, if she don't wanna be with me and wants Rambo Kramden instead, let her go on 'bout her damn business. Besides, it's her loss, so fuck it!" But sometimes, men ARE their egos. So, when my ego reminded me she'd stopped answering my calls around 10:50 p.m. and it was now 12:45 a.m., I said "Fuck that! It's been almost two hours." Nobody had to know I was a weak-ass punk unless I told them, so I was out the door.

She lived five blocks away and I was so emotional that I ran all the way there. I viewed all the parked cars around her building to see if there was one I didn't recognize. There was, and it was probably his. She lived on the third floor and her apartment overlooked the street from two angles. One window was her living room and the other was our bedroom. The light was on in the living room, so it was confirmed. I ran home and called her and surprisingly, she answered in a calm voice. I asked what she was doing and she said she was talking and sipping on some champagne. My worst nightmare was coming true. A playa was about to get played by Pretty-Monster and Rambo Kramden!

I ain't gone lie. I ran over there about three or four times that night just to see which lights was on. The last time I ran over there the bedroom light was on. I think I actually flew home that time (Lol!). I had to have wings, fast as I got there and called her. I asked her if she was in her bedroom. She was like, "Yeah...how'd you know?" "Cause I just know and you can't play me! And what the fuck is he doin' in yo' bedroom?" "We're just sitting on the bed." To me, that was just like fuckin. Man, I was dying inside. "Well, what's wrong with the couch?!" Then, she went straight off on me right in front of Rambo. "Look here muthafucka! This is my goddamn place! You don't live here and you don't pay shit here. I can have whoever the fuck I wanna have, in any room I want...and I just know you ain't been spying on me?"

My pride was hurt, so I had to save face. "Hell naw, are you crazy?! Bitch, I ain't got to spy on you. You and that niggah both can kiss the most -bitter part of my sweet, raspberry black-ass and bark at the hole. I can have any fine-ass woman I want. I ain't gotta spy on yo' ugly muthafuckin' ass!" "Ok, then why you keep calling me wanting to know what the fuck I'm doing then?" I had to pause because she had a very valid point and she broke me down right in front of Rambo. I was humiliated. But, she was telling the truth and I was just lying trying to save face. "Now, don't call back here no more tonight!"

Another great lesson I learned during this phase of my life was how women tend to speak between the lines. Or, shall I say, I learned to read between the lines. You see, when she said, "Don't call back any more tonight", I took it literally to mean THAT night. I'll have to admit, I shed a few tears that night. But why, I really don't know. I wasn't in love and I wasn't pussy whipped. Maybe because it was the first time (that I knew of) someone was able to get MY pussy, and my ego was bruised. I'd finagled other men's pussy, but never the other way around. Either way, I discovered I was a sensitive playa. And, what's the first rule of thumb when you're selling drugs or pimpin'? Don't get high off your own supply. Here I was dating a 'bugar-wolf' as my girlfriend? Was I crazy, or had I just lost track of who I really was? I mean, I was 'da man', right? So, I had to flip the script and get back on track.

The next day she told me she and Rambo ended up falling asleep in her bed. Of course I asked if they fucked. She claimed they didn't but that they only embraced each other with their clothes on. I didn't believe her. But at that point, she didn't have to lie to me, especially after the way she went off on me the night before. That would have been a perfect follow up for her, "Yeah, I fucked him. So, now what?" It was all good though. My worst fear was now over.

We continued seeing each other and I continued spending the night just every now and then. I even got used to sleeping alone in my own bed back at my mom's house. P.M. and I were getting along as well as we ever had and even continued fucking. Hell, I even reverted back to my original hour long sessions. I merely desensitized my emotions because she wasn't mine and neither did I own her pussy. I was just the one she was giving it to. She felt me pulling back and started questioning me. She was always extremely jealous and somewhat accusatory, but while some of that was me seeing other women (which I sometimes did), much of it was her low self-esteem. Whatever the case, I was back in the right position and just about ready to let her go. You see, I discovered I like being the one to end relationships when I have the upper hand. I also discovered once I've taken all I can stand...I'm done! But first, I had to have a showdown with Rambo Kramden.

From Boy to Man

I noticed how P.M. ceased talking to Rambo on the phone. In fact, his periodic calls seemed to unnerve her. This, of course, boosted her feeble self-esteem knowing some old dude was damn near stalking her. But, her facial expressions seemed to exhibit a realm of fear which alarmed me. So, I asked her what was going on between them, not out of jealously, but as a concerned friend. She told me the novelty had worn off from her perspective, but he wanted to continue seeing her. I guess it felt good for an old dude to have a 'young tenderoni' giving him some time and attention. She might have been a 'bugar-wolf' to me, but, one man's trash is another man's treasure. My ego told me she dumped Rambo because she wanted our relationship to continue. One particular night, Rambo just kept calling to the point where even her roommate started asking questions. It seemed like the situation brought the three of us closer together because, above all else, we were all friends who graduated from the same high school.

Later on the same night as I was about to go home, P.M. just about begged me to spend the night. Something in my spirit told me to take my ass home. You see, the more I stayed home the more my morality kicked in and my saved conscious returned. I was trying to stop fornicating and the best way to do it was by staying out of precarious situations. However, against my better judgment, I stayed. And once we were all asleep, her apartment buzzer rang. I knew it was Rambo, so I immediately got in whoop-ass mode. But P.M. asked me to stay in the apartment while she went down and talked to him. You know I wanted to fuck him up anyway for all the previous stress he'd caused me and for waking me up that night (yeah, I was just looking for any reason).

I gave her about seven minutes, then I just had to go downstairs. I quietly descended the stairs as not to be heard because I wanted to hear if her account of what happened between them was accurate. As I got to the point where I could see and hear them, it was evident her story was authentic. Neither of them could see me, so I just continued to listen. He had his back to the door and she was in front of him but facing me. When she attempted to come inside from the vestibule he grabbed her and her facial expression indicated she was in way over her head. So, I instinctively stepped in.

"Hey my man, you ain't gotta put yo' hands on her. If she's finished talking to you, that's it!" It was the first time I'd ever seen Rambo and HE was a "bugar-wolf" TIMES TWO! That muthafucka looked like something from, "The Hills Have Eyes" (the original movie) and smelled like cigarettes mixed with alcohol. I thought to myself, "If he and P.M. ever had a baby together, it would look just like "Hell Boy" and they could sell pictures to the National Enquirer!"

Rambo replied, "Aey mane, 'dis here ain't got nothin na do wit' chu!" "It does when you start putting yo' hands on her." He came right back at me. "Niggah what?! Look here mane..." Then he squared-off on me, and in the ghetto that's taken very seriously (that's when a person widens their stance to throw a punch with more leverage). At that moment, as I looked into his glassy eyes it was extremely apparent he meant business. Then, I suddenly remembered why I nicknamed him Rambo. This niggah used to KILL people in Vietnam. Yeah, he was a government-trained ASSASSIN. But hey, it was too late now; I had already committed myself to stepping into a grown man's shoes. So, even though I was a little nervous, I had to play it on out.

In these kinds of situations, religious people turn to prayer and I was no different. I heard the voice of GOD in my head. "See there my child...I told you to take yo' dumb-ass home, didn't I? But you just refused to listen." "Yes Lord I know, you're right as always and I'm sorry for disobeying you. Please forgive me Father for I have sinned. And oh yeah, GOD, can you make sure this crazy muthafucka don't have a flash back from Nam? Amen!"

But, then I noticed something out of my peripheral vision. P.M. loved every minute of this shit--two men apparently fighting over her ugly ass. Now, that made me mad and embarrassed as hell within myself because she wasn't worth it. At that moment, she asked me to go back in so she could handle things. This was my opportunity to break. But, I was a man so I had to end it like a man. "Are you sure?" "Yes, I'm sure." I looked at him one last time as if to say, "Don't start no shit, won't be no shit." He looked at me and rolled his eyes as I walked away. I was satisfied with how I'd conducted myself like a man in that situation. I stood at the bottom stair just to make sure she was alright. But she asked me to go back to the apartment and wait for her. I suddenly felt like the entire thing had been orchestrated by her. I was so pissed and at that very moment, I knew I'd had enough. I went up and got the last few belongings I still had there and left. I walked home content. In fact, I felt great! I faced adversity like a man that night, and was satisfied. Plus, I was young and handsome with a promising future and I walked into it and away from Pretty Monster--the "bugar-wolf"--forever.

Movin' On

A year or so went by as I seriously pursued my collegiate studies. I was young, good-looking, healthy, confident and intelligent. I was stylish, fashion-conscious and hanging out with all the honeys. However, I kept the "fireman's helmet" in my pants. It's a funny thing about Moor (black) men. We oftentimes give our penis names. It's mostly the result of high testosterone, ego and the result of women blowing our heads up...literally and figuratively. Some Moor (black) men actually get real creative with it. For example, some might call it 'the truth' and have a motto to go along with it like, "You can't handle the truth."

Nevertheless, my religious convictions enabled me to remain celibate. I was one of the rare men actually waiting to get married before engaging in sexual intercourse. I know you're probably saying, "You were just shacking up with a 'bugar-wolf' in the last chapter, now you're abstaining?" Well, that's how the religion thing goes. People TRY to live holy by not sinning.

But, fornication seems to be one of those sins apparently a whole lot of religious zealots have difficulty controlling. It's partially because they really DO want to have sex because it feels divine. Now that's ironic. And, sex feels even better when you're brainwashed to believe its wrong and instructed NOT to do it. You're guaranteed an extra orgasm based on that alone (Lol!), especially if you sneak and do it. And, the intensity is really multiplied when it involves someone who's...involved.

But, religious people continue to live under the pressure of convincing the saints (church people) they're holy enough to NOT have sex. They're all in denial. Don't get me wrong, I've lived in celibacy on several different occasions in my life and at one point, for as long as four years. And, while it was potentially harmful to me because as it relates to your body, what you don't use you lose, at least I wasn't exposed to the possibility of STD's or something much worse simply because I wasn't sexually active. So, celibacy has its place, only when it's for a short period of time and for a specific purpose, for example: soul searching, revitalization, emotional, spiritual, and mental cleansing. Hypocrisy is NOT one of those purposes.

When a natural, human function is suppressed or denied, it usually creates a counteracting perversion. Just ask some of the catholic priests. That's probably why you'll find some of the freakiest, most promiscuous women in the church. They're in denial about desiring and needing sex. They simply love it, but have been brainwashed to believe it's sinful unless they're married. Unfortunately, this is a major reason why religious people get married too soon and for the wrong reasons. They're looking for the legal, lawful and moral permission to have sex. Sometimes you can pick up freakier women in the church than you can at the club; you just need to know how to speak the language: "Glory Hallelujah! Praise the Lawd and bless you sister! May I have your phone number...in the name of Jesus?

Batteries Included

Religious lady by day
Delicious woman by night
Weak day morality...just a formality
Weekend bitch trying to live right

Clean thinking...clear thought
Lusting for the toy I just bought

Battery-operated lover
Vibing with a freak undercover

I want a real monument
Tall and erect
But this lifeless form
Has become my norm
It can't harm me...and it won't reject

I'm tired of being hurt
Too discouraged to search
Sanctified fags up in the church
And 'dem pretty ass niggaz don't wanna work

I refuse to accept the down low
And I don't know what's coming next
Just wanna good man that's faithful to me
To know I'm having some real safe sex

Battery-operated lover
Vibing with a freak undercover

My excuse to be loose
When I'm all by myself
Energizer keeps me going and going
And I ain't cummin' for nobody else

I'm Sunday morning saved
But Monday morning hot!
And tempted by Tuesday
To pull it out the box

Weak all day Wednesday
Thirsting Thursday for an erection
So freaky by Friday
Duracell has my affection

Oh yeah...and uhh...one day of rest
As I do my very best
To convince the world and myself...that Jesus is the only man I need

At ages 18 and 21, a real psych-job takes place. Color of law defines 18 as the legal age of consent. However, in essence, it means absolutely nothing and according to your personal situation, you understand that it doesn't. For instance, if you're still living at home or with somebody who's paying for your sustenance at age 18, YOU'RE NOT GROWN despite the prevailing psychology convincing you otherwise. But in reality, even YOU know the truth. So, while you're allowed to vote (for the best liar), and dorm in an adult penitentiary if convicted of a crime (which is really all turning 18 means), you still must wait to become a "certified adult" to purchase your own liquid poison. And even at 21, if you're living at home or with someone who's paying for your sustenance, YOU'RE STILL NOT GROWN! However, at 21 you have this insatiable need and desire to prove to everyone, excluding yourself, that you're a real adult. Unfortunately, this is usually accompanied by a long series of dumb-ass mistakes, like dropping out of college, misusing credit cards, getting married and making babies just to name a few. Well, I did all of that, and a whole lot more.

All Grown Up?

Ok...so you say you're all grown
And you wanna be left alone,
To do what the fuck you wanna do?
But instead of havin' yo' own...

You're still livin' under a roof that isn't yours
As you resist parental reigns over you
Rules and regulations seeping through your pores
Now you ain't nearly the adult you thought you were...before

...We kicked yo' fake, wanna-be grown-ass out into the real world
Now, you can show us you're the grown woman you claimed to be
And not that immature lil' girl
We always see.

Yeah Bro, tough love kicked yo' ass right out the nest
Uh-huh...that and all your blatant disrespect.
So, since you're man enough to live on yo' own...
Flap yo' wings brotha, and oh yeah...be blessed!

So you really think you're ready for the fast lane?
Make damn sure you are, or prepare for the worst kind of pain
You know a hard head makes a real soft ass
And right now, yo' ass is like butter on the noon dessert plain

Here you are still a few years away from twenty-one
And already a dirty holster for every young gun
Lookin' to shoot cum
Into where you say you ain't trying to go
Pretending to be a lady
But, all yo' Johns calling you a whoe!

Already been plucked by a plantation full of cotton-pickers
At least that's the word on the street
Can you blame 'em for calling you as they see you?
Need to be real careful about the company you keep
Cause they don't give a fuck about the real you
Just want you to perform like them strippers do
And when they're through
They'll put you in the who's-who of who to screw
When they're looking for somebody new to 'do it' to.

Or when they need a public toilet
Somewhere to take a 'quick squirt'
Haven't you realized that's equivalent to pissin' in the dirt?
Someone to squirt in
Someone to shit on
And after they get on

You walk the fuck home

So after whoeing yourself...later in life, when you're all done
Having what you considered to be so much fun
Now you expect prince charming to come along
To make you an honest woman for himself
After you were a whoe for everybody else?

Naw, lil' man we ain't judging you
Though you're lacking sound judgment
We're just nudging you
To open your genetic memory bank
Before yo' mouth write a check yo' ass can't cash
Hoping in the very near future you'll awaken the GOD in you
And, manifest your DIVINITY into the present
Placing all your childish immaturity in the past
Then, you'll be that adult we all recognize...at last!

Fresh Out of the Wrapper

On a winter evening in 1988 while in a study hall at the university I attended, I was made to notice this attractive young lady across the room. I was thoroughly checking her out while trying to decipher some French homework. But, what really made me pay attention to her was when she left the room. She had the nicest pair of legs I'd ever seen on a sista and I wasn't even a "leg man." [For whatever reason men have a tendency to classify themselves by the woman's body part they like most. Now, I'm a "butt-man," but primarily a "womb-man".]

When she re-entered the study hall I decided to talk to her. However, I was a bit apprehensive because the room was packed, and you always have to account for the fact that Moorish (black) women might clown you. Y'all know what I'm talking about. Depending on her mood, she may try to humiliate you, and I'm not good in those situations. I mean, rejection is one thing, but humiliation? Nah, I'm just too sensitive for that. At some point she discovered I was diggin' her because she got up two or three more times to offer me a better view. I simply enjoyed the twist in her hips (in fact, I always appreciate when a woman puts a twist in their hips just for me. Back then, I thought women owed it to me because I was "that guy". But now (in the present), I consider it an honor and a privilege. It's like a mating call and I think it's special for a woman to go that extra mile just for me).

I stuck around way longer than I intended to, so I could gather my game plan. When it was time to make my move I left the room and attempted to get her attention from the hallway. It took a few minutes (though to this day I believe she just wanted to make me wait. You know how women can be.). Once she finally responded and came into the hallway, I put my extra special 'mack' down on her to which she responded very favorably. She was different...a little wacky and very innocent all at the same time, sorta like Lucille Ball. So, I'll just call her LB.

LB was a shapely size six, medium-brown beauty with flawless skin. Her full, broad lips and dimples created a wide smile encompassed within her squared-jaw line and clef chin. She had a perfectly proportioned body accentuated by nice, big legs that could've only hailed from Down South stock. Her shoulder-length, fine hair texture was just a few steps removed from Indian hair. She had a semi-deep, raspy voice which made her sound very sensual. LB was the kind of woman who didn't need much to accentuate a very natural beauty and she had the capacity to even look good on her bad days.

Since I started stage acting at five years young and went professional at 13 years young, by age 21 when I met LB, I was a seasoned veteran on the stage. And because of that, I could really illuminate my personality at will and that day she got a full blast of it. Well, coincidentally she was also a thespian. That had to be a sign from GOD. You see, one of the many unfortunate disadvantages associated with religiosity is people expect a GOD external of themselves to do everything for them, even things they can only do for themselves, (you know, like thinking and deciding), and they look for signs as CONFIRMATIONS for what they desire most. That being the case, initially noticing LB was a sign, and the fact that she had nice legs was yet another sign! The twist in her hips and the fact that she was a thespian was all a sign from GOD.

We started dating like it was the end of the world, then the strangest thing occurred. For a couple of weeks straight, we wore the exact same colored clothing (tops and bottoms) without planning it. Now, that was a sign and a miracle (Lol!). How could we have chosen the exact same colors so consistently without it being some kind of divine intervention? She was attractive and very smart with a good family upbringing. I mean, she was studying to be a doctor for GOD'S sake! That had to be a sign, right? Well, that's how I perceived it.

LB was actually starring in a production when we met and our first date was watching her perform in the play. She was (just) alright. I mean, she wasn't star quality like me (Lol!). After the run of that particular play, I went with her to an audition for another play. The guy slated to play the lead character was really good. He was doin' his "thug-thizzle," and was also extremely afro-centric and I could tell he was real intelligent (he graduated from high school as valedictorian and class president), and he was also an aspiring rapper. In fact, he went on to some notable fame and fortune in the rap industry.

...

[A few years later, I saw him at a chemical plant. He docked a truck for a load of chemical compound produced by the company I worked for. When I recognized him, I initially felt a little embarrassed for him. I wondered how a guy that made such significant strides in the rap industry could've been relegated to being a mere truck driver. I conversed with him for a few minutes and he told me he'd utilized his earnings from the rap business to buy a fleet of trucks. He owned and operated his own trucking line. He said being on the road as a rapper was highly overrated and it wore on him very quickly. He also said he didn't know where the rap game was headed and questioned its longevity. So, he thought ahead and established a legitimate (lucrative) business. See, I told you he was real intelligent.]

...

I attended a couple of rehearsals with LB while mentally rehearsing the way I'd play the role myself. After one particular rehearsal, the lead character gave the director his schedule and discovered some of his personal business dates clashed with the production schedule. They departed thinking things would somehow work out. But once the lead character left, the director panicked. "I need to find an understudy, somebody who's good and professional who can pick up real fast."

LB told him I was a thespian, even though she hadn't seen me perform. He raised an eyebrow. "Really now?" He enquired about my acting dossier and I ran it down to him and he asked me to audition right on the spot. Now remember, I'd been to a few rehearsals and had been mentally rehearsing the lead part all the while. One thing about me, I'm most comfortable on stage (my problem is once I'm off stage...Lol!). I gave it to him with "both hands in the face." He loved my acting ability! He actually said, "Shit, fuck the understudy; I might have the lead character right here!" He immediately started trying to figure out how he could cast me and the other guy as we alternated shows. But once the other guy got wind of it, he dropped out. Besides, he had a whole lot of other more important things brewing in his life. So, LB and I were officially starring in the same play...Lucy and Ricky.

Now this had to be another big sign, right? I distinctly remember LB appearing a little jealous of the attention the director was offering me, and it started to show in her performance too. The director started riding LB's back pretty hard about her lack of energy on stage, and in strict contrast, I was gambling. Meaning, I always tried new and different things on stage to enhance my character and he simply adored my every decision.

I had complete autonomy on stage, and that's the way I liked it. He also had high praise for the woman who played my grandmother. She looked much older than her age and was a good actress too. She was only

22 but had the ability to play someone three times older. She sort of looked like Biz Markie with long hair and she stank like a muthafucka! Then she had the nerve to spray perfume on top of her stench! That was my only problem with her. You know she really must've smelled pretty damn bad for me to remember her funk 20 years later! LB and I used to talk about her hygiene all the time when we were alone. We also gave each other funny looks during rehearsal, but I don't think she ever realized we were talking about her.

The play toured for a short time, and I was in heaven, getting paid for what I loved to do and hanging with LB. One night she and I were chilling at my (mom's) house and just before she was about to leave, I kissed her and it swept LB right off her feet. I was becoming infatuated with her and came to identify her as a real, good girl. LB had attended a historically black college and accepted internships at Harvard and Princeton Universities. She was studying to be a doctor, but had plans to become a neurosurgeon. LB's dad and other family members had doctorate degrees, and a blind man could see she was heavily influenced to follow in their foot steps.

LB was a 'good girl' alright; I primarily saw her that way because she was a virgin. Now, for a religious guy, that was the sign of all signs. I mean, you just don't find attractive 21-year-young women with that kind of pedigree, who are also down-to-earth and fun-loving, without being conceited or boule AND a virgin! She told me her mother (who was deceased) and grandmother brainwashed her and her sister to get married before having sex... period! Well, they damn sure must've put an Uzi to her head because she wasn't giving up shit, which appeared to increase her value to me.

Girls, women, ladies, princesses and queens, listen up! (Goddesses y'all already know.) If you really wanna raise your status and value--with boys, men, gentlemen, princes, kings--save the pussy until you've completely captured their heart. If he can't wait, then fuck him! Not literally, I mean if he's not willing to wait, let him go on about his business. However, if you can't or don't wanna wait, then just be real about it and say so. Yes we truly wanna fuck you and would love doing so if you LET us. But, there's a small remnant of respect that's lost when you initially say "no," but then turn around and 'give up the drawers' Sometimes that's why a straight-up whoe can foster more respect from us, because at least she's up front about her sexual desires and motives and not perpetrating the fraud. Even though we may not customarily take 'em home to meet mama, we at least respect their honesty and straight-forwardness.

Yes ladies, when given the opportunity, we will certainly use the shit outta you if you LET us. But remember, in the game of love, sex and romance, there's absolutely NO victims! We'll also value and respect you along with your decision to wait if you MAKE us. Keep in mind; you hold the keys either way. So, let your 'yes' be yes, and your 'no' be no. Either be an authentic good girl or a straight up whoe. That being said, I offered LB the utmost respect by never taking my hands below her waist. Initially, I didn't move my hands below her neck, until she gave me permission to do otherwise. I remember intimate times kissing until our lips damn near fell off, and I might get a portion, and I do mean a small portion, of titty. We'd dry grind (fully clothed) until my dick was sore and swollen because it was very clear LB wasn't giving up shit! I'll have to admit, at first, I wasn't fully convinced she was a virgin. But, after several scrimmages, I was thoroughly convinced and had to follow suit. I started viewing her as a keeper. I mean, how could I possibly not take a serious look at LB as an outstanding prospect for marriage, even at my young age?

LB and I were inseparable and even though I felt good about us in general, and about her in particular as a potential long-time prospect, after six years my heart still belonged to A.L.E...hands down! During my courtship with LB, I noticed a definite decline in A.L.E.'s calls and letters. I was still calling her and writing occasional letters and while her roommates were very cordial as they received my messages, A.L.E. didn't return my calls. And, the few letters I did receive from her were very short and predictable, almost like it'd become routine. I mean, I realized she was in college where guys were very aggressive, and I knew she was pledging a sorority, so the frat boys and the upper classmen were probably all over her. Maybe she'd given up her virginity and just hadn't told me.

It had been about five months since I'd heard from A.L.E. at all. It

80

kinda concerned me, but I didn't let it consume me because LB was present and accounted for. Although there were some subtle comparisons between the two of them, LB was no doubt a VERY distant second place to A.L.E. I wanted to offer LB my full heart and mind, but I needed to hear from A.L.E. first before offering mental and spiritual commitment otherwise. I gave A.L.E. a silent ultimatum (in my mind) with a time limit. "Now look here, if I don't hear from you within a month's time, saying you love me and all our plans are still in effect, I'm moving on." Or, I just needed to hear her say she'd found someone else worth marrying and wanted to spend the rest of her life with them to substantiate me committing to LB.

I met LB in early February 1988 and around November of the same year, we started talking permanency. What can I say? We were young and infatuated. By then, I was in real good with her family. Her younger sister was pretty cool and I had her dad's favor. I guess her father knew we were getting serious as he threw me out of his house later and later every night (Lol!). He used to laugh and shake his head at us, maybe because we reminded him of his humble beginnings with her mother. Now LB's dad was HILARIOUS, though not in a comedic way. He just had this real down-to-earth way about himself that was very matter-a-fact. Plus, he was born and raised in the deep-country South, but spent his adult life in big northern cities. So as a result, he possessed a southern refinement with a northern cool. He was extremely handsome and charming, a real ladies-man type, and the ladies loved him! He was very dark, around 6'4" and weighed about 250 pounds with broad shoulders. But, he was about the nicest, kindest man you'll ever meet. He was a Pediatrician and really seemed to like and care about young people. But, I really noticed how extremely caring, considerate and patient he was toward LB and her younger sister. No matter what they did, he'd end up either laughing with them or at them.

For example, LB's 18-year young sister eloped while she was still in high school. Most of her family (including us) was absolutely appalled. Her boyfriend was a silly young boy who was still living at home with his mom while LB's sister still lived with her dad. She'd been married for a while before she told anybody. Initially, her dad was very upset and even more disappointed. But then, I guess he just figured it was already done so they ended up laughing about it. Later on, he told LB and I he knew we were smart enough not to do anything like that. We both suspected that was his way of telling us not to do what they'd done.

His kindness, consideration and patience toward LB and her sister didn't appear to be merely because their mom was killed in a car accident months before we met. It appeared to be an authentic part of his personality and nature. He'd also recently picked up a new girlfriend who really seemed to adore him. I'm sure in many aspects she was conducive in helping him stay grounded. I could tell he eventually appreciated my frequent, lengthy visits to his home because it enabled him to do his own thing away from home with minimal anxiety. So, it worked out for the benefit of everybody. I was happy for him and he was happy with me.

I knew he trusted me when he started leaving us there home alone, although he did unequivocally tell me he didn't wanna catch us in any 'compromising situations' in his house. Let me tell you, he looked a whole lot bigger when he said that as I was sitting on his couch. Little did he know, there was absolutely nothing for him to worry about because his daughter had a padlock on the pussy and I didn't have the key or the combination. The den where we usually frequented overlooked the driveway, so we could see him pulling up which gave us ample time to stop doing whatever we were doing, if anything at all. Occasionally, he'd park in the front and come barreling through the front door in a rush, no doubt to throw us off guard. That used to tickle the shit outta me because he'd head straight to the den. But after several months, he chilled out and everything was all good.

On a warm afternoon in December of 1988, as LB and I were riding around discussing our future, we decided to elope. And although we'd mimic the same (foolish) actions of her immature lil' sister, we promised not to make the same big mistake of telling anyone. No one had to know and we'd just carry on as usual. The primary difference would be our moral permission and legal right to have sex (Lol!). It was about 3:01 p.m. and we figured the Toledo, Ohio municipalities closed around 4:00 pm. Usually the drive from Detroit to Toledo was a little less than an hour drive.

Well, we got there in 40 minutes, rushed in and got married.

I had a strange feeling I was doing something wrong, or at the very least, something premature. But when you think you're grown you often-times make childish mistakes and decisions and it was confirmed when this little tongue-tied minister performed our ceremony. Neither of us could understand a damn word he was saying. Shit, I don't even think HE knew what he was saying (Lol!), because sometimes he would just smile after attempting to pronounce a word that none of us could recognize or understand. I kept saying, "I beg your pardon" so much until I just started saying, "Huh?"

Something in my heart and soul was saying, "Stop! What the fuck are you doing? Get yo' dumb ass outta here, right now! It was GOD. Neverthe-less, we went on with it. We both must've realized we made a wrong or premature decision because the ride back home was dead silent. She was driving so slow it took us well over an hour to get home. I mentioned a motel we could visit to consummate our marriage, but I also made the drastic mistake of telling her I'd previously frequented the motel. Man, what the fuck did I do that for? We had the biggest argument about it and with me being so anxious, immature and insensitive I couldn't understand why. So what I had fucked around with some woman at the same motel. It wasn't like she was gonna be there with us, or the motel hadn't changed the sheets since then. But in LB's mind, she'd remained a virgin until she got married and simply refused to have it cheapened or compromised. So she decided to postpone our consummation until we (she) could enjoy a more appropriate honeymoon. Shit, I'd waited this long so a few more weeks was no big deal (Ok, I'm being facetious. It was a huge deal!) We were newlyweds living in separate houses and it was our big secret.

Lucy…I'm Home!

A week or so after LB and I eloped I received a call from a very cheerful voice. It was A.L.E! Oh shit! I hadn't heard from her in about five months and she was bubbly as ever. I couldn't believe it! She was so excited to talk to me. I couldn't get a word in edge-wise, and she was saying all the things I wanted to hear. "Hey baby, ooh I miss you SO MUCH!!! I have really been thinking about you and us. Hey, guess what? I'm planning a trip to come and see you! That's right, and I GUARANTEE these plans won't fall through because we're not teenagers anymore baby. We're real adults! I'm almost outta' college and I don't need my parent's permission anymore! Me and my sorors are gonna drive up there...and you and I are gonna have our own hotel room.

I just got home for Christmas break, but I'll be up there real soon to see you, baby! I'm planning to stay a whole week! That way, I can get acquainted with my future mother-in-law (laughter). I talked to her yesterday. Did she tell you? Oh baby, I haven't lost my virginity yet, but I ain't gone lie, I have COME CLOSE a few times, but I didn't. I broke up with my boyfriend because he was soooo immature. He kept askin' me to give him "some." Come to find out he tried to get with one of my sorors. She's a skank-whoe anyway. He couldn't get any of 'THIS' because he didn't deserve it, because I'm saving all 'THIS' for my baby! Oh God, I am SOOOO horny for you! Trust me! We WILL make up for lost time. I was just so darn busy with studying for finals and doing term papers and pledging...shoot! It got so overwhelming.

BABY, I only have another year to graduate! Then we can finally be together....forever! Can you believe it's been six years???!!! And people say long-distance relationships don't last. You can come live here, Ontario's nice. Or, I can come there, or we can move somewhere else altogether different. I don't really care where we go, as long as we're together. You know what? I saw this really cute little boy with curly hair the other day and I immediately thought of our children. Baby, we're gonna have such a big happy family. Hey, my sister's always asking about you and stays on me about keeping in touch with you. She says you're a good man. Oh, my mom just said hi.........Baby what's wrong, why are you so quiet. Aren't you glad to hear from me?"

I was shocked it was A.L.E. and simultaneously mesmerized by her cheerful, sensual, British-accented voice. Have you ever in your life come to the absolute conclusion that you've unequivocally...FUCKED UP? Where you saw it in your mind and felt it deep in your heart that you've totally done the very opposite of what's true and right and really, really... FUCKED UP? Well, that's what I felt like.

So many things ran through my mind: annulment, lying to A.L.E., abandoning LB. I was speechless and stuttering at the same time. I sounded like the tongue-tied minister who had performed my marriage ceremony. "Uhh, baby? I uhh, have something to tell you." Now, in hindsight I should've got an annulment, especially since I hadn't consummated my marriage yet, apologized to LB, allowed A.L.E. to come and visit, impregnated her, then moved to Ontario and married A.L.E. But, unfortunately I was religious and therefore moral, and obviously very stupid. So, I felt compelled to tell her the truth. Damn, we live and learn don't we?

Both eloping AND telling A.L.E. I got married are two of the biggest mistakes I've ever made in my life. "Uhh...A.L.E...Baby...I got married." There was dead silence in the phone. I thought I was going to die because I felt her pain through her silence. As if she didn't hear me the first time, "What did you say?" "I said...I got married." She was in a total state of shock. "When did you get MARRIED?!" My heart was in my stomach. "Uhh...last week." "WHAT! You got married??? But why did...," then she dropped phone and started crying, but I could still hear her mom in the background. "What's wrong A.L.E., is he alright?"

A.L.E. picked up the phone and covered the receiver as she replied to her mom. In a split second I tried to drown out her mother's words with my feeble explanation. "A.L.E. baby! Please listen to me. I hadn't heard from you in so long and I didn't know where we stood, and you weren't returning my calls and your letters weren't the same. A.L.E. I'M SORRY! Please listen to me. Baby, I'll just get an anul..." Then I heard their conversation over her crying. "Mama, he said he got married." "What!!! Oh my goodness! Just hang up the phone A.L.E., hang up the phone!" "Wait A.L.E., please don't hang up! Let me explain!" Then there was a dial tone.

I held the phone for about an hour replaying the whole incident over and over again in my mind. I sat there on the edge of my bed...in my mother's house...married to a woman I didn't live with...feeling sorrowful because I had broken the heart of the only women I'd ever loved...knowing I'd never see or hear from her again. I knew full well I had fucked up royally! It felt like my entire destiny had been redirected at that very moment, like my future had suddenly ceased and I began to live day to day.

Later that week LB was over and as I was looking for something in my bedroom she found the shoe box full of A.L.E.'s letters and began reading one. "What's this?" "Hey, leave that alone, those are just some letters from a good friend of mine who lives out of town." Then she smelled the box. "Well, why do they smell like perfume?" "Because I guess she sprayed perfume on them (duh!)." "Oh, well she certainly wrote you a lot." Then she started irritating the shit out of me by counting them. "There's over 48 letters here" (and she was right because A.L.E. wrote me about eight times a year over six year period). "Why are you being so nosey, can you just leave shit alone?" "Well, I have a right to look at them after all, I am YOUR WIFE!" That ripped through me like a straight razor, but she was right. "You can throw these away now because you don't need them anymore." LB must've been out of her fuckin' mind! Those letters were the only part of A.L.E. I had left and I was certainly not about to throw them away. But LB put up such a fuss about it that she gave me an ultimatum. "You either take these out to the garbage right now or I'm cutting them up." As much as it hurt me, she was right, and since I didn't want her desecrating A.L.E.'s letters and pictures, I tossed almost a third of my life history into the dumpster.

It took about a month before LB and I consummated our marriage. Why? Because she was scared it might hurt, and it did the first time. But, it got better very quickly. We'd been married a couple of months living in separate houses and still nobody knew our secret. Those were the fun days! She was either over my (mom's) house or I was over her (dad's) house. Only thing was we couldn't spend the entire night together, but other than that, there was no pressure, no pain and no strain. We were just saving money and making plans. But, living in separate places and not spending nights together as a married couple made LB anxious. So, she became very argumentative. But I came to know that arguments and disagreements are unfortunately a part of marriage and I needed an outlet.

A good friend and I started bodybuilding, mainly because we were both skinny little ballerinas (Lol!), but also because it was a macho, stress-relieving guy thing. He was 129 pounds and I weighed 131, which was the heaviest either of us had ever been. But, we were both the same size... extra small. We started off pumping up every day and we were really intense about it. Jeff was strong as hell to be so small! I was the weak one. He used to laugh at me because I couldn't bench press 90 pounds. Jeff was benching 135 (anything over your own body weight is pretty impressive) and spotting me as I struggled with 90 pounds. That was so embarrassing.

A few months after we started, our work and school schedules changed so we couldn't work out together for a while. But, I continued working out two to three hours a day, five days a week. I went from 135 to 150 pounds in four months, but couldn't' seem to get any bigger. So, I asked some of the trainers in the gym for pointers. I'd been a vegetarian for a couple of years and one of the trainers told me that in order to get big, I had to eat meat. I did just that, and over the next five months, I went from 150 to 188 pounds. I was buffed as hell at 5'8".

I remember stopping at red lights while driving and people on either side of my vehicle would stare at my muscularity. All the extra attention was pretty fun from women and men. There's just a certain amount of respect given to a 'big fella,' and that's whether he's big and tall, or just plain big. Even women who previously wouldn't holla at me because of my size was blowing horns and givin' me a holla. No harm, no fowl though. I mean, I was religious, morally upright, and therefore totally faithful to LB, so it was all in good clean fun to me.

I was a maniac in the gym. All the big guys and pro bodybuilders in the gym started calling me 'big fella.' Now THAT was my dream come true! A few of the pros even let me work out with them. You know, it's funny how those very same guys never said one word to me or Jeff when we were both tiny ballerinas struggling with light weight. They didn't even speak to us. But, once I put on 57 pounds of muscle in less than a year, they all started speaking to me, holding conversations and helping me with the heavy weight. I guess it was one of those fraternal macho guy things. I was also taking muscle supplements, which helped me get bigger and stronger even faster. By the time Jeff and I started working out together again, I was 188 pounds with 15 % body fat and was benching over 200 pounds while Jeff was still struggling with the light weight. Guess who was laughing now?

Getting a house so we could be under the same roof was LB's daily topic of discussion and it caused frequent arguments. Personally, I had the best of both worlds and wasn't necessarily in a rush to change it, but she was. Little did we know something tragic would happen that would expedite her desire.

One particular morning I was at LB's and we were engaged in one of our daily arguments. It got to the point where her dad even intervened. He would often shake his head and laugh, "Y'all act just like an old married couple." Every time he said that, we used to think he knew we were married because he said it so much and his laugh really made us suspicious. Well, on this particular day he flipped the script and said, "Maybe y'all should take some time apart from each other." We both looked at him like he was crazy. When he noticed our matching expressions he reiterated, "Well, I mean, y'all can't seem to stop arguing, maybe y'all seeing too much of each other...just like some old married couple." Then, he shook his head as he turned around and walked out laughing. We both thought that was so strange. Yeah he knew it. He just had to. I took his advice and at least left for the remainder of the day. I told LB I'd see her later on, but unfortunately that was the last time I'd ever see her dad...alive.

Life Happens

Later that afternoon, I went to the gym as usual and remembered our earlier argument. LB just needed to be more patient and we'd have our house real soon. That evening I remember talking to one of the guys in the gym about woman issues. I didn't really know him all that well but I guess

I just really needed to dialogue with someone who could relate to masculinity. I really didn't work out that much for running my mouth, which was extremely unusual for me. I was a "gym rat" come rain, sleet or snow, so I did at least enough to get a pump.

I got home well after dark and laid my sore, sweaty exhausted body on my bed. I was staring at the ceiling with my hands behind my head and my feet crossed, contemplating when I was gonna get up and take a bath, when the phone rang. It was my sister-in-law and she spoke in a real quiet, solemn voice like she was drugged or something. "Heyyy, we been trying to contact you at your house." "Yeah, I just got back from the gym." "We figured you were there. I know you gave us the gym number before, but we couldn't find it and we couldn't' think of the name of the gym." "Oh, ok, well what's going on?" "Well, my faaather got killed this evening." "What! Where's LB?" "She's here with me." "I'm on my way there." "Ummm, we're not at home. We're at Rosy's house."

Rosy was a friend of their family. I was in shock. "Oh shit! What happened?" "Weeell, we don't really know all the details yet, we just know he was shot on the way to his girlfriend's house." "Shot in the car? Was he car-jacked?" "Naaww, he wasn't driving; he was walking." "Somebody robbed him?" "That's what we originally thought, buuutt all his money and stuff was still in his pockets, so it wasn't a robbery." "Well did they catch 'em?" "Naaaw, they don't have anybody in custody yet and they don't have any witnesses or leads yet either." "What the fuck? Ok, I'm on my way. What's Rosy's address? Wait a minute, why didn't LB call me? Put her on the phone!" "Sheeee doesn't feel much like talking; I think she's feeling bad. My dad gave her his car to drive because she asked him to use it, and that's why he was walking. Now she feels like it's her fault that he's dead." "Damn! So, she's feeling guilty?" "Riiiight!"

My blood ran cold in my veins because I didn't really know what to think, whether it was some kind of a hit, or if someone was gonna try to come to the house and kill them or what. I got the address from my sister-in-law and raced over to where they were. I rang the bell quite a few times before anybody answered the door, which annoyed the fuck out of me since they all knew I was on the way! Rosy FINALLY answered the door.

...

[Rosy and I didn't particularly care for each other or get along. For starters, she was nosey as hell (nosey Rosy) and always trying to run everybody's business, especially as it related to LB and her sister. She was real boule' and materialistic too, always bragging about what they had. You know, like she was so much better than everybody else. And that alone irritated the shit outta me. I mean they (she and her husband) had nice money and lived in a prime neighborhood, but she didn't seem to have any class to go along with it all. She was borderline obnoxious. She was actually LB's mom's long-time best friend, but it seemed apparent to me that Rosy wanted to fuck LB's dad. She stopped by LB's house at least three times a week (with or without her husband) being real flirtatious toward LB's dad. It was so obvious. I mean, LB's dad was real handsome and charming, but he was her long-time, best friend's HUSBAND whose wife hadn't been dead that long! Plus, she was married her damn self! Now, don't get me wrong; she was a very sexy and attractive woman. But damn! Have some scruples!

I could tell there was a strong (sexual) vibe between LB's dad and Rosy. I'm not a voyeur, but Id've paid good money to see 'em go at it. I'm sure it would've been better than a porno. Maybe that was another (hidden) reason why I didn't like Rosy, because I wanted to hit it too but knew I never could. However, the greatest reason for our mutual disdain was that we both were trying to influence LB and neither of us wanted to lose out to the other.]   ...

Anyway, Rosy finally opened the door. "Hi, LB doesn't feel well or feel like talking. Maybe you can see her tomorrow." Now this was the last straw! So I pulled rank on that bitch. "What, excuse me!? But uhh, tell MY WIFE to come to the door right now, please!" Rosy was shocked because she thought she knew every (damn) thing about everybody's business and she was appalled that something so important had obviously been withheld from her by someone so close. "Your wife?! LB you got company!" Yeah, I finally let the cat out of the bag, but it was long overdue anyway.

I talked to LB for a little while, trying to assess her mental status, but I didn't stay too long because I didn't feel welcome and I wasn't about to kiss Rosy's ass...not even in her own house. Before, I left my sister-in-law congratulated me on our marriage and asked why we didn't tell anybody. She was going through a divorce because her marriage didn't last very long, but none of us really expected it to. "Well, I really hope you alls last. My dad used to always say y'all acted like an old married couple." Then she chuckled. "I think he knew y'all were married." "Yeah, we think so too." Then I went home.

The next several weeks were very trying for us. Not only did we have to endure two separate funerals, one in Detroit and another Down South where her dad was born, we also had the added anxiety of not knowing if the culprit would attempt any further harm to the family. Plus, our families were discovering our not-so-new marriage and many seemed a little disappointed. They all kept asking the same irritating ass question: "Did her father know?" After a while we just started telling people that he knew, which prompted the question of why he never told the rest of the family like when his youngest daughter eloped. It was all real fucked up.

I started spending the night at LB's house, because it was the natural thing to do given the situation. I reminisced back a few days to when I told LB to be patient because we'd soon be living together, but neither of us had any idea it would be this soon and under these circumstances. LB and her sister welcomed me there and it was a good arrangement for all of us. They felt much safer with me being their protector, and by this time my mom and I were having major arguments at home. It was just time for me to leave. And her three-times-a-day motto was: "If you don't like what's going on here, get the fuck out!" That used to burn my anal canal, as it does most wanna-be adults.

Deep inside, you know your parents are speaking the truth. But you're either too unprepared, immature or afraid to move out and that's when they use psychological warfare against your ego, which is almost foolproof, at least for a man anyway. Well, it all worked out perfectly. I was spending so much time at LB's that half my stuff was already there. One Sunday morning my mom and I got into it big-time...she was in rare form and she put some extra stank on her famous motto until it reverberated in my head like an echo. "GET THE FUCK OUT! Get The Fuck Out...get the fuck out...get the fuck out!" It was at that very moment I really heard my mother and shortly thereafter, she went to church. Now, isn't that ironic? She cursed me the hell out and called me everything except a child of GOD, then went to church to "praise the Lawd" (Lol!)! As soon as she left, I packed all the rest of my shit and bounced! Everything was NOW official. I was married living with my wife...in the same house.

You never really know somebody until you live with them. I've always heard that "shacking" was a sin and I used to believe it (though I'd never seen it in the bible). But now that I know better, I think differently. I think it's only intelligent to live with someone you're planning to marry to discover whether you have a real chance of staying together. LB was the worst! She was a complete slob to the third power and worse than the sloppiest guy I knew. She didn't wash dishes until every dish in the house was used. We'd end up drinking out of pots and eating with butter knives. It was so crazy!

When she washed clothes she never followed the directions on the labels on the clothes. She'd mix blue jeans with white clothes and wash them in hot water and the white clothes would come out blue. Or, she'd put chlorine bleach in colored clothes and they'd end up with white spots. But, all of these things were considered hilarious to her. I told you she was like Lucille Ball and unfortunately I was Ricky Ricardo. People always used to say they thought it must've been fun being married to her. Yeah, it's funny when you're on the outside looking in, but when you're IN all the antics, that shit ain't funny at all.

But through it all, I did what a Christian man was supposed to do...take full care of the 'Eve' because she was the weaker vessel. I carefully mimicked my granddad's lifestyle and paid for everything. LB worked everyday but didn't pay for anything, I even bought her clothes. I kept her 'shaaarp as hell' while I stayed G'd to the max. I had my suits tailor-made back then, I had two jobs and was going to school full-time. At 21, I really took adulthood by the horns. LB's parents had done well for themselves and owned a mini-mansion in the historical district of an upscale neighborhood. So, in essence we were doing pretty well by virtue of us inheriting his estate. We each had brand new cars and one would've assumed we'd live happily ever after. However, I learned there are certain realities in marriage you must be keenly aware of. First, arguments are unfortunately an integral part of marriage. Secondly, romance without finance is ignorance. Third, wives often use sex as bait, leverage, a weapon, or reward for (fill in the blank). Next, husbands are ALWAYS wrong while wives are ALWAYS right. Fifth, you unequivocally can NOT win an argument with your wife and even if and when you do, you actually lose (see number three...Lol!). Sixth, arguments and disagreements will increase just before, during and after your wife's menstrual cycle. Seventh, sometimes in marriage, you'll feel very isolated and alone.

A Bad Marriage

Should I trust someone who says they don't' trust me,
though I've given them no distrust to qualify?
Should I think about someone lovin' me,
while sexing my spouse who I'm disgusted by ?
Should I masturbate more now
than before I married someone who doesn't like making love to me?
Are these tears of joy I'm crying
as I'm lying
in my bed
Next to a warm pair of legs
feeling oh, so lonely?

I quickly discovered that LB was either very immature, irresponsible, spoiled or damn selfish; I concluded it was a combination of all four. She was rapidly showing herself to be counter-productive as it related to working together in a marriage. But following in the footsteps of my grandfather, I emulated his fashion of completely taking care of my wife. Though we didn't have a mortgage or rent to pay because we inherited our house, she made damn sure all the other bills were exorbitant to make up the difference. Actually her dad left the utility bills 'on swoll' apparently he didn't believe in paying the full bill, so our light, gas and telephone bills combined were over a thousand dollars a month. LB and her sister kept the heat on 90 degrees during the cold months (which is seven months out of the year in Michigan), and kept every light on in the house all night long. I was working midnights then and distinctly remember coming in most mornings from work cutting every single light off in the house...even closet lights (Lol!).

I bought all the groceries, paid for house repairs and LB had the unmitigated gall to get mad at me when I refused to buy her a new car! Now keep in mind, she had a good-paying full-time job, but didn't pay for shit! I told her she had to buy her own new car, but I compromised by paying her car insurance. Initially, I was giving her the money to pay all the bills until we started receiving overdue notices. About two months passed before I realized what was going on. I asked her what the hell she was doing with all the money. She said she had been shopping at the mall. Ooh, I was mad than a muthafucka! So from that point on, I just started handling our finances. Her irresponsibility only furthered my disregard for her as the weaker vessel. LB was either careless, lacking sound judgment which (in my estimation) made her weak and vulnerable, or she was very inconsiderate and conniving which made her evil. Either way, she left a very bad impression upon my psyche regarding her as a woman.

There was a brief few months of indifference that was temporarily comforting to me (sometimes the marital experience can be pretty indifferent: it isn't really good and it isn't really bad, it just...is). Things really began to change after that. LB started taking me for granted. She had the attitude like, "I got him now so I can exhale." And when she symbolically let her hair down, I definitely didn't like what I saw. Ladies please hear me: whatever you did to get him (should've been the real you in the first place) needs to be maintained to keep him. LB's first and foremost priority became her sister. I guess she felt responsible to be at her every beck and call since both of their parents were now deceased. It was like THEY were married and even though I understood the concept of caring for her sister it didn't quite sit right with me. It still felt like she was committing adultery on me. Even worse, her sister started blatantly competing for LB's attention and allegiance (that also didn't sit well with me) which created animosity between me and her sister.

As I described in my 'humble beginnings', I have an insatiable need to feel special and when I don't, I must either resolve the issue that's caused the change, rid myself of the person, or leave the situation. And at the young age of 23, my patience was extremely low and my tolerance for bullshit even lower. By this time LB had totally let herself go. She didn't keep a tidy house and every single thing under her control was in total disarray including herself and her hygiene. I kept telling her to snap out of it and I waited for it to happen, but after a while I discovered this wasn't an act or a phase. This was the real her. I wanted to use the death of her mom and her dad's murder as valid reasons for her bizarre behavior and (unwelcomed) changes. On top of that, LB would have real violent fits of rage which usually ended with me restraining her from behind as she bucked and fought to get loose. She unequivocally did NOT know how to handle her anger and if it weren't for me being the disciplined man that I was, after witnessing domestic violence as a child, she definitely would've got her ass whooped on several occasions. But, I loved LB and I felt sorry for her because she didn't ask to be in this situation. I was just trying to stick it out and stay with her...at least until I couldn't anymore.

There must be something real sexy about a young married man because women were jockin' me from every direction. I mean, don't get me wrong, I was buffed, handsome, attractive, intelligent, had a mini-mansion, a brand new car, working two jobs, in my last year of college, well-dressed with a wonderful personality and sense of humor, young and very married. Who wouldn't want this total package? But all that lured women of every nationality and walk of life to try me? I mean they were throwing pussy from the free-throw line (Lol!). I truly believe when you're content in a relationship and have no desire to be with anyone else, people tend to be attracted to that energy. I was fighting women off left and right, at work, at school and at church. Everywhere! Now for the record, I was totally faithful to LB to the highest degree and never fucked around on her, not even mentally, because I believed what the bible described...that it's a sin to even think about sin. And I was one of those religious muthafuckas that took his shit real serious. I was saying 'no' more than a fine-ass woman at the club.

I took interest in film-directing in college. I spent a lot of time shooting videos and short films, fortunately for me (but unfortunately for LB), gorgeous, fanatical women were a serendipity of my interest. That's just the nature of the business. It seemed like every woman wanted to be in front of the camera, in a video or movie, or at least know someone who was involved with it all. Initially, LB was cool with everything, but after a while she became ghetto-jealous–that's when the jealous party goes buck-wild and starts tearing shit up. And since she already had anger-management challenges, it made for a real bad combination.

For example, one afternoon we got into an argument about a (female) classmate of mine who called the house after 11 p.m. Well, I told her to call me after 11:00 because I was working afternoons and didn't get off till then (duh). Now, this was before the cell phone age, so it made good sense to me. But LB bitched and moaned about it that night, then nagged the shit outta me most of the next day until it erupted into a full blown argument. In the midst of the argument she said, "I ain't no whoe, so you need to go find you one!" To which I replied, "I already have one." I was referring to LB, but she thought I was referring to my classmate and she went straight off!

She got so upset she went upstairs and got her dad's pistol. Shit! I didn't even know there was a gun in the house. I guess I was fortunate I hadn't pissed her off to that extent before, or she might have done it sooner. Anyway, she came down stairs teary-eyed and frantic, thinking I had been fucking around, and pointed the gun right at my head at close range. I couldn't believe this bullshit! I felt like I was in a damn movie. Ironic huh? Remember the scene in the movie "Goodfellas" when the main character Henry woke up in bed with his wife pointing a gun in his face and he had to talk her crying, frantic ass out of shooting him? Well that was me, but it happened 20 years before the movie came out (Lol!).

96

You gotta remain real cool and calm in those kinds of situations because showing any resemblance of fear or intimidation could prove fatal. So I went G-Mack on her ass. "Put that damn gun down girl, what da fuck is wrong wit' chu?" Then, I had to put a psyche job on her crazy ass. "Just look at cha, you don' lost yo' damn mind. You're outta control!" Then she started crying and the gun started shakin' in her hand. Now I'll have to admit I got a little nervous, but at least I knew I was inside her head. I just needed to finish the job. "I tell you what, I'm gon' call the police and let them deal wit' chu crazy-ass." And I actually called 'em too.

"Hello...uhh, yeah I have a woman pointing a loaded gun at my head at 1313 Mockingbird Lane." "We're dispatching cars right now!" "Now, they'll be here in a few minutes so you can explain what the fuck's goin' on and I ain't gonna let you embarrass me in front of our neighbors either." Then, I casually got my jacket and headed to the front door. Now THAT was a smart move right there! I kinda figured if she hadn't shot me in the face, she probably wasn't gonna shoot me in the back of the head on the way out the door. But make no mistake about it, she definitely could've and would've shot me if it wasn't for (my) Divine intervention through quick thinking.

Yes, it was true I didn't wanna be embarrassed in front of my neighbors, but my main objective was getting the hell away from her crazy ass with that gun. She followed me all the way to the front door crying with that shaking gun pointed at the back of my head. When I closed the front door, I heard LB run up the stairs no doubt to hide the gun. I started walking down the street and sure enough, about a block away, I saw three police cars speed past me on the way to my house. Needless to say, I didn't return until late that night. But that's the kind of shit that happened being married to LB. I knew then that we were at the beginning of the end, but I was trying to hold out to salvage our union.

Now on top of that, LB was the worst fuck of the century, not that I had a world of experience to compare her to, but dayum! She was what men call a dead fuck! I would say she was also sexually repressed. Remember, she was a virgin and had absolutely no experience (and little to no passion). Or, maybe I just wasn't her cup of tea? Nah, I was "the shit" so that couldn't have been it (Lol!). Personally, I think from a sexual perspective, I may have showed her too much, too soon.

Although I only had a relative few years of experience, my 'explicit-nature,' imagination, intense sex drive and raw passion were all well ahead of my years in reality. Often times, during or after our sexual encounters, LB would look at me like I was crazy and ask, "What kinda women have you been with?" Or, "Where did you get THAT from?" Sometimes she claimed she couldn't fully enjoy our lovemaking knowing that I'd been with other women before her. I told her I couldn't change that. Then she'd make the comparison that she'd maintained her virginity, while I'd been a whoremonger.

LB was horrible at giving head, she was squeamish about me going down on her (but since her hygiene sucked worse than she did, it was only a one-time offer), she didn't like it doggie-style because (she said) she couldn't see my face and felt like she wasn't a part of the act. The first and only time I tried the 69 position she called me the devil (Lol!), and missionary style bored me after a while. Plus, missionary style allowed me to see her patented, you-fucked-other-women-before-me expression she displayed so often during sex. Lastly, it wasn't really effective when LB rode me because that's an assertive position for women and she definitely was not sexually assertive in the least bit. So in essence, she was the complete worst! But it didn't matter because she was my wife, my only sexual outlet and I was young and viral. So with me being young, dumb and full of...cum...I put her on a regular schedule of three times a day, five days a week. Poor LB...or should I say poor me. That alone was worth a divorce, especially when you considered all the other madness she initiated. But there was at least one last major event that caused the demise of our union.

Oh, Really Now???

One afternoon I came home and there were two Moor (black) men in my living room. They were well-groomed and conservatively dressed in cheap suits. One of them was particularly handsome and speaking very attentively to LB and her sister. I'll refer to him as 'Handsome Harry'. The other gentleman was looking at a number of pictures displayed on our mantle, but not like he was admiring the photos, more like he was looking for clues. I initially tarried in the living room for a few seconds to get a feel for who they were and what was going on because strangely enough, they all sort of carried on as if I wasn't there.

Through reasonable deduction I surmised the men were detectives offering updates on the facts surrounding my father-in-law's murder. After a few more seconds of talking, the men slowly started heading for the front door as I ascended the stairs. As I got half-way up the stairs, 'Harry' addressed me by my last name and extended his hand. I descended a couple of stairs to shake his hand though I was a bit irritated, cause I felt he was being a bit condescending, and he could've said something before I got half-way up the stairs. "I'm detective whatever-the-fuck-my-name-is and we wanted to know if you'd be willing to come downtown for some questioning? We've spoken to just about everyone else surrounding the case."

I looked down upon everybody who was fixed upon me awaiting my response. I was a bit curious though, so I glanced over at LB and her sister, and then replied to the detective, "So everybody's being questioned?" He glanced over at LB and her sister and responded, "Uhh yes, they've already been questioned." Then LB and her sister chimed in, "Yeah, we've been questioned already." I found this to be quite strange considering neither of them had mentioned anything to me about it. So I went along with it. "Yeah sure, I can come down." He handed me his card, and as I looked ahead to his partner, I discovered his eyes had been sharply fixed upon mine the whole time. It was all a real strange, brief encounter but I couldn't really put my finger on the odd components that bugged me.

After they left I questioned LB. "Why didn't you tell me you went down for questioning?" "It really wasn't anything to tell, just some routine questioning that's all, no big deal." I just stared at her for a few seconds until she realized I knew she was lying, but we were on such bad terms by then, it really didn't matter.

A couple of days later I went downtown to the police station. As I entered the large office, there were five Moor (black) detectives all suited up and staring in my face. Suddenly, I couldn't imagine any of the other people supposedly questioned having had this kind of reception. 'Harry' was sitting on the topside of a desk with one foot on the floor right in front of the chair I was expected to sit in. He motioned for me to sit down and initially I was seated so close that he invaded my personal space. So I moved the chair back a little but I knew that was some ol' macho, ego bullshit. I then recalled why he irritated me so much. I distinctly remember him being a little extra kind and nice to LB when he was at my house. LB had a lot of personal issues but she was still very attractive. So, I didn't know if he was being disrespectful trying to push-up on her in my house (which would've been a lot of nerve) or he was just attempting to agitate me. Either way, I never gave him any outside emotion to examine.

Once his partner began talking he got up and sat topside another desk. "I'd like to ask you a couple of routine questions if you will." Then he silently gazed deep into my eyes for so long before continuing, it felt uncomfortable. "Where were you on the evening of the murder?" "I was at the gym working out." "Oh, do you work out a lot?" "About four days a week." "Yeah that's good. Gotta stay in shape, huh? Do you always work out in the evening?" "No, it varies depending on the day." "I see...and does the gym have a roster or a sign-in sheet of some kind?" "Yes all members have to sign in, per visit." "Oh, so you have a membership, huh? Ok...did you uhh...sign in on the evening in question?" "Uhh, I'm sure I did. I usually do. Sometimes I forget but I'm pretty sure I did." "Hmm...ok." Then he wrote something down on his pad. "So if we were to check, your name would definitely be on the sign-in sheet?" "Yeah, I'm pretty sure."

"Do you remember talking to anyone in particular or having a particular conversation?" "I definitely remember the conversation, but I'm not sure if the guy I talked to was an actual member. The strange thing is that I didn't really work out very much, that day. We did more talking than anything which was bizarre for me because I'm usually pretty focused at the gym." "What was the conversation about?" "Women and relationship problems." Now it was at this point that the Divinity (in me) took over.

You see until now, I was totally oblivious to what was REALLY happening, but then I was made to notice a few things. The other detectives in the room were literally hanging upon my every word. I could see them through my peripheral vision on either side of me. I could also see 'Dirty Harry' slowly shaking his head as if he disagreed with my answers. The room was uncommonly silent, to the point where our voices sounded like they were in stereo with extra reverb. Then I realized the questioning detective had a very smooth, calm, soothing quality to his voice that was almost hypnotic. I could tell he did this shit for a living and was damn good at it. But the thing I remember most was the way he stared right between my eyes like he was peering into my very soul. He never blinked and he never looked away unless he jotted notes on his pad. It was at that time I realized he wasn't just asking me questions, but rather...I was in a line of questioning.

Once I became aware of what was happening, I experienced a plethora of different emotions: anger, betrayal, and fear just to name a few. However my Divinity wouldn't allow me to display an outward manifestation of fear because doing so right then and there could've meant my ass. My Divinity instructed me not to panic, but to relax and remain calm. I told myself not to fidget or squirm and above all never, ever break eye-contact with the questioning detective. So, I peered into his soul as he was peering into mine. I also realized why 'Dirty Harry' had purposely been trying to agitate me from the start, to perhaps invoke a response that could've incriminated me (I suddenly felt like Nino Brown in New Jack City when he stabbed the knife into Kareem's hand, "I never liked you anyway...pretty muthafucka.")

He continued, "Did you and your wife argue on the day of the murder?" "Sure." I shook my head so matter-of-factly it sort of caught him off-guard. I could tell he anticipated a different answer. "Do you and your wife argue pretty often?" I nodded once again. "Well of course. Sometimes, too often." Now, he certainly hadn't anticipated that response and I could sense the other detective's total focus. "Hmm...really, why is that?" I tilted my forehead forward and simultaneously raised my eyebrows before I replied, "Are you married?" "Uhh, yes I am." Then, I leaned my head to one side and raised one eyebrow as if to say, "Duh! That's what married people do." He obviously understood my non-verbal communication because he slowly nodded in approval of my honest answer. He chuckled to himself as he wrote on his pad. "Yes, I certainly do understand." The other detectives obviously felt the same because they all nodded as well.

He asked me a few more questions to which I responded openly and honestly until his cold, hard stare became warmer and his hypnotic grip lifted from me. "Well, I think that's all the questions I have for you today." Then suddenly ol' 'Dirty Harry' made a dramatic outburst of disapproval like the lead character in a bad theater production. "Naw, uh-uh...hell naw!" He got up from the desk he was sitting upon and stormed toward me with his finger pointed like he was about to interrogate me LAPD-style. But the questioning detective, who was older and apparently wiser, lifted his hand and motioned for him to stop right in his tracks. He then continued, "If we have any other questions for you we'll give you a call, ok?" But, "Harry" just couldn't seem to let it go and interrupted once again until the questioning detective looked him right in his face and slowly and very deliberately shook his head in disapproval. I took his gesture to mean I was definitely NOT the culprit, and he was right! Then, one of the other detectives grabbed 'Harry's' arm and pulled him back. "Just let it go man. Let it go."

It was vividly evident and obvious to everyone else that I was innocent. So I looked across the room at him in a semi-condescending fashion. He looked like he really wanted to whoop my ass or something. As I was exiting the room, the questioning detective told me, "Take care of your beautiful wife man. She really seems like a nice person. I know this situation has been difficult for her, so try to be patient with her." I turned around and responded, "Yes she is...and I will, thank you." Yet, in the back of my mind I countered...yeah, she might be beautiful and a real nice person, but her days as my wife are definitely numbered, because I'm about to wish her MONKEY ASS to the corn-field!.

As the months rolled by, I continued to be the good provider and loyal husband I'd always been. But our love-life slowed to a snails crawl, by my own doing, because I simply refused to have sex with LB out of sheer spite.

On the rare occasion when we did, she was always the initiator. Our schedule went from three times a day, fives days a week to (eight minutes) once every three weeks, which was more than fine with me especially since she was the worst.

My spite ran deep because whenever we argued and she found herself on the losing end of the argument she would say, "I think you killed my father." Or what really used to burn my anal canal was when she'd directly ask me, "Did you kill my father?" That shit used to make me so fucking mad and she knew it! It also used to hurt me deep down to the core. But I don't think she ever knew that because I was very adept in disguising my hurt and pain with sarcasm, so I made it seem like it never really bothered me. I lost all respect for her as a person and much love for her as my wife. She morphed my (already) demented view of women into a total disregard and disrespect. She became the poster child for everything I loathed in women.

One day I called her out on it. I told her, "You're either extremely stupid or horribly nefarious." She said, "What do you mean by that?" I said, "Because if you really thought I killed your father why are you still with me unless you're a dumb-ass and a damned fool! Only an evil-ass bitch would continue to say some shit like that if she really didn't believe it. So which one are you...a dumb-ass fool or an evil bitch?" She stopped and thought about it for second then an angry expression came across her face because I'd placed her in a rhetorical catch twenty-two. Checkmate! She smooth cursed me out for about five minutes straight because she knew I was right.

When we first got married, LB's initial complaint was that we weren't living together in the same house. Her gripe was understandable though. I mean, a married couple should live together, right? But after that was resolved and a year or so had passed, her new campaign became "Let's buy a house." Her rationale for that was to let her sister have the 4-bedroom mini-mansion with the two-car garage despite the fact that her sister didn't have a car and couldn't drive. LB wanted her sister to assume the $1200 light, gas and phone bills without a job? I mean, she was getting a little SSI check for her handicap, but it wasn't nearly enough to sustain herself. LB claimed she wanted us to have privacy and her sister to have the independence she craved. But her sister's hearing impairment made her extremely dependent upon LB (which she often took great advantage of). LB would be spending so much time helping her sister in a practical way, not to mention financing her independence, that it wouldn't make sense. So, the whole idea of us buying a new house and moving was absolutely absurd!

LB claimed she wanted something we bought as opposed to something we inherited. I told LB it would make more sense to get a little apartment for her sister and help finance it. In the back of my mind, it seemed like she was trying to set up two places to live between. And, depending on which place was most comfortable and convenient for her at any given time, that's where she would reside. Or, at the very least, it was a way of getting me out of what she considered her house.

I kept fighting to save a marriage which I realized I couldn't save. I hoped things would somehow turnaround so we could recapture what initially attracted us to each other. I continued hoping for more patience to deal with all the madness and stayed optimistic that LB would regain her sanity. Here's the irony: deep inside I wanted out, but I refused to initiate the divorce because it was against my religious beliefs. So, I stayed 'in it to win it' though it was a losing cause. I'm sure it wasn't easy for LB either...or her sister for that matter. There was always a lot of tension in the house. They argued more than we did, so it was always the Fourth of July around there. It was probably toughest for LB because she was catching it from both ends and refereeing spats between her sister and me. Then, after a while, I just shut down totally.

One thing about me is that I'm a natural communicator and very eager to express my opinions and sentiments, so if and when I shut down...it's a wrap! So between that, and me withholding sex, and us sleeping in separate bedrooms, and me working full-time with two part-time jobs and being away from home a lot, LB was officially very unhappy. That's when her frequent chants of divorce increased. I kept telling her that she was gonna have to initiate it because I refused. Then I told her if she wasn't really gonna do it, then shut the fuck up talking about it. But when she reached her apparent limit, she did what I wasn't brave or honest enough to do: file for divorce. Actually, I was a little surprised. Hell, I didn't think she'd ever do it especially since she was causing most of the shit. She cried wolf about it for so long, a couple of years went by and I never took her seriously. And, even though I wanted out, it still felt strange when I got served.

So, I prepared to move out while wrestling with my emotions. Most people thought I had the happiest, most adorable little marital situation. You know, two young people finishing college, living in a nice big home with two new cars and four jobs between us. Everybody thought we were the shit, except for the few of our very close associates who knew differently. I loved our façade though I was catching plenty of hell. I was also quickly becoming very wonderfully anxious about my potential new single life and living with peace of mind. And just when I thought I had a handle on the entire situation, I was thrown a curve ball.

By Who??? Girl, Bye!

During this time I was working midnights and on occasion LB's old college boyfriend and his sister would stop by in the evening. He was a short little light-skinned guy with sandy-brown hair and a high ass. He seemed a little soft to me, but otherwise seemed like a nice guy. His sister was a shapely 'yellow heafa' about four years younger, but she was a sexy lil' beast and you could tell she was hot to trot. I think besides the fact that they were close siblings, he kept her with him to keep her out of trouble. In essence, she was looking to get fucked and he was doing his best to 'cock-block' for as long as he could. He'd bring her over to get counseling from LB or she would just chill out with my sister-in-law who was her best friend.

LB and his family were real close. Sometimes he'd come by himself and they'd all be laughing and talking as I left for work. On occasion when I came home for lunch at 2:00 a.m. they'd still be talking. That never bothered me because I was real secure with myself and the man that I was. I figured, if LB maintained her virginity through four different colleges of horny young guys applying their sexual pressures, an old friend wouldn't change her character, especially as a married woman. So it wasn't really the fact that I trusted her so much over the fact that fidelity was just a part of her character.

Also, if a woman's gonna fuck around on you there's really nothing you can do about it, whether you're aware of it or personally witness it. It is what it is. And, with LB being the absolute worst in bed, he would've almost been doing me a favor. In the back of my mind I figured if we ever got divorced he might be a prime candidate for her rebound rendezvous. I often wondered why things didn't work out between them since they seemed to get along so well. So one day out of curiosity, I asked LB and she said it was because of the distance between their respective colleges for one thing. But my sister-in-law ended up telling me that LB had tried to kill him when he broke up with her. She said he decided to dissolve their relationship during the time LB's mom was killed in a car accident, which she considered really bad timing so she tried to run him over with her car. I was shocked and immediately thought back to when she put that gun to my head.

LB had a REAL history of anger-management issues. My blood ran cold in my veins thinking about how her crazy ass could have really shot me. That was when our demise became official for me. I said to myself, "Why couldn't I have discovered this before I married her crazy ass?" Since then, I've always asked any woman I was seriously dating if she's ever killed anyone or tried to kill anyone. That's just one of those basic things I need to know if I'm gonna seriously consider dating them (Lol!).

I guess my sister-in-law must have told LB about my surprised reaction, because not so long after arguing one night, I woke up in the middle of the night and LB was standing over me. My normal impulse, while disoriented and startled like that, is to wake up swinging. But she was very fortunate I saw it was her. She just stood there, still, creepy, purposely trying to spook me out, then she left the room. I was mad as hell, but too sleepy to respond. However, the next evening when I recalled the incident I let her have it. "And you almost got yo' ass fucked up last night! The next time I wake up and you're standing over me, I ain't gonna be responsible for my reaction! In fact, from now on don't even come in my room without knocking especially if I'm sleep!" I could tell by her facial expression that she took my words very seriously. Shit, I had to let her know she didn't scare me. However, from that point on I slept with a butcher knife under my mattress...just in case.

Early one morning about 6:00 while I was still at work, I received a call from LB. She said she was nauseous and had regurgitated and thought she might be pregnant because she'd felt the same way on consecutive mornings. "By WHO? Girl Bye!" fell out of my mouth before I could catch myself, because my mind was so far away from that, besides I couldn't remember the last time we'd had sex. And of course that pissed her off. "By YOU, fool! How the hell you gon' say something like that?" She was actually calling for me to bring home a pregnancy test. So I did and she was. I couldn't believe it! But I maintained my plans to move out because her pregnancy didn't change the fact that our relationship was fucked up, and thus our marriage. It's funny when couples say their marriage is bad, like marriage is an entity all by itself. It's the relationship between the two people that's the foundation, and the marital union is derived from that relationship. So the union can't do, or be, anything without it first emanating from the relationship.

She asked if I was still leaving and I was like, "Uhh, yeah!" Then she went through this long soliloquy about how she needed help and couldn't do it alone...etc., etc., blah, blah, blah. I told her she didn't ever have to worry about me taking care of mine, but she was actually talking about having me there throughout her pregnancy. I really wasn't feeling that, but I asked her, "So what are you asking me to do? Stay here until you have the baby then leave?" She said, "At the very least." I thought that was the dumbest shit in the world, but it was all good because it gave me more opportunity to stack my chips so when I finally moved I could do so very comfortably.

In the back of my mind I questioned her damsel–in-distress change of heart, which was very different from the wolf-tickets she was selling when she served me the divorce papers. It was uncanny how we had sex three times a day, five days a week for almost two years without any form of birth control measures whatsoever and she didn't get pregnant. Then suddenly, while having sex once a month for eight minutes at a time, as I'm focused on moving out, divorcing her and returning to a single life, she pops up pregnant? It just didn't make sense to me. Hell, maybe her old boyfriend was hittin' it. But I didn't really worry about it because the truth would show once the baby was born. After all, there was always the trusty old blood test. So I agreed to stay. And I took a real vested interest in LB, specifically since she was carrying my future generation. I knew her emotional status during pregnancy would impact our child. So, I really tried to make sure she ate right and stayed comfortable and she didn't do anything too strenuous. But strangely, we started becoming more cohesive. We started liking each other again and I guess we both started feeling like our unborn child would help reunite and keep us together. You think like that when you're immature and impressionable. I mean, we were only 24 years young.

LB was perhaps the most stunningly beautiful pregnant woman I'd ever seen. You know how some Moorish (black) women really morph into something ugly during pregnancy with dark circles under the eyes? Their noses spread wide across their faces and their necks get crusty and turn darker and they gain too much weight? Well, LB actually looked more radiant and beautiful during her pregnancy than she ever did. The quality of her flawless skin complexion improved as it glistened and glowed. Her medium-brown eyes lightened to a hazel hue and her Indian-hair texture grew longer and flowed with a supple sheen (I sound like a damn cosmetic commercial, don't I?).

LB actually had trouble gaining weight because she couldn't' keep anything down; in fact, she didn't really pick up any significant weight until her sixth month. So she maintained her shape. I remember taking her and my sister-in-law to my company picnic. I was so proud. Everybody commented on how beautiful LB was. We actually had a pretty good time, too. I remember sitting in the warm evening sun absorbing her femininity, and recalling...maybe we could make things work. GOD knows, I had the motivation to finish what I had started, even if I lacked the patience. I was committed to staying together and compromising my personal happiness just so long as I wasn't completely miserable.

She is Life

She's not just with child...not just giving birth
She is LIFE
A microcosm of the macro universe
The cosmos is a replica of her inner being
She is the bearer and giver of life
In her we define and refine our self-worth

There's absolutely no life without You
We owe our existence to NUT, the feminine principle of NU
The creator, initiator and sustainer of our sons and daughters
The bark of millions of years floats upon your primordial waters
Many lives reside inside of LIFE
She is indeed the first who shall always last
Onto the future becomes the present
And, the present becomes the past

Your nurturing nourishes humanity
Great Goddess who begets goddesses & gods
We're enlightened by your alchemy
Comforted by your staff and chastened by your rod

    I spent many evenings talking to LB's stomach communicating with my son. Sometimes I'd talk at her vagina because I didn't really know where he could hear me best, but I definitely knew he could hear me because he'd respond by moving around. You learn a lot about the female gender through pregnancy. I observed LB's natural instinct to sacrifice her personal comfort for our son's benefit. I observed that as an innate feminine characteristic and not just a part of LB's personality. I paid close attention to her body and the way it transformed and adapted to accommodate new life. I studied her emotions, which were many and ever-changing, and observed the power her emotions seemed to possess over my own.

I felt the intense mesmerizing effect her femininity had upon my masculinity. It felt stronger, more dominant and more divine. There were moments when it seemed like my masculinity was subordinate to her femininity. Yeah I fertilized the egg, but that's about it. She did everything else for my son for the duration of her pregnancy, while I merely watched. So how could I beat my chest, as a man, claiming so much sovereignty over this miraculous event when I played such a minuscule role? I dismissed these thoughts as foolish and unfounded. I mean, how could these thoughts have any validity when women are the weaker vessel and subordinate to man? Hmm, something within me knew these and other radically progressive thoughts would resurface in the future.

I was present and accounted for as my son came into this world. I describe his so-called birth that way because in reality he was already very much alive before conception. Once my sperm cell penetrated his being it merely transformed his estate. Just think about it. An egg is alive within a woman even before the solarplasmic energy cell (liquid sun) known as sperm initiates the mitosis process. So abortion is straight up premeditated murder because a child's birth into this material world is the transition from its cosmic existence, to its amphibious nature, to this (lower) material existence we call humanity.

Life…Before Death

It was dark…

T'was warm and cozy…inside

Everything I needed was right there before me…because I was well-connected

Didn't have a care in the world, for I was not yet of…this world

Just surrounded by DIVINITY on every side.

Back then…I could breathe under water

Submerged in the fluids of my Feminine Creator's life

My third eye wide open deep into my own world

Eyes tightly closed to my universe within the multi-verse called Heaven

Soon to descend into the hell of light and strife

…I died onto life

And after death…I am alive

I gained so much respect for the female gender watching LB have our son. It was rough just watching her labor, so I can't begin to imagine how tough it was for her actually giving birth. All I know is, I was SO glad to be a man! I think if it were up to men to replenish the earth, there'd be about 12 people on the entire planet. And they'd all be only children. My son was (supposedly) 11 days overdue and didn't seem to care. In fact, he required some assistance to be evicted from his humble abode. But, like most tenants who are evicted, he didn't leave without tearing some shit up (Lol!).

You see, because he was supposedly overdue (and thus, bone-dry) and there was absolutely no lubrication to slide him through the birth canal, they placed a suction cap on the top of his head and literally yanked him out. As he exited, friction from the dryness tore LB from her clitoris all the way down to her anus. I jumped and cringed when I heard it rip. It was literally one big hole. That was one of the most incredible things I'd ever seen in real life.

Two nurses held a sheet to catch my son as they yanked him out. I thought it was a little unorthodox but, whatever you gotta do, right? He did a complete flip and landed on his back, bouncing on the sheet like a trapeze performer falls in a safety net, and was indeed bone-dry. His eyes were wide open and he never whimpered or shed a tear. I thought that was unique to say the least. He was staring at the ceiling until my emotional out burst of, "Wow!" turned his attention toward me. He turned his head to me as if he recognized my voice, and he did because of all the nights we communicated through LB's stomach. Our eyes locked and I felt a special bond occur.

At that moment, I knew I didn't wanna move out or get divorced. I wanted to be home to raise, protect, nurture and cultivate this new life I was now responsible for. They sat him in a deep sink to wash him off and he hadn't cried yet, but I thought he would once the water hit him. Not so. He just yawned a very adult sigh of relief like he was taking a warm shower after a hard day's work. I chuckled to myself...What kind of baby is this? Yeah this was my son for sure, and there was absolutely no need for a blood test because he looked just like me (minus the hair on my face... Lol!).

In the meantime, LB was being sutured. It took an hour and twenty-seven minutes to completely sew her up. After the nurse wrapped my son in swaddling clothes they placed him upon LB's breasts, and for the first time since coming into the world, he cried like somebody had pinched him. I took note of that particular moment and thought to myself...it was a bad omen.

It was very evident that I'd had a change of heart about leaving. I'd never said anything to the contrary to LB, but she knew it. She could see I was enamored with being a father; I still am to this very day. Marriage took on a whole new vibe. It felt like I was really married. I had so many plans and ideas for my son. I didn't wanna give him any of the same old fucked-up status-quo: philosophies, traditions, morays, folkways and poisons that my parents gave me--like Christmas, Easter, the tooth fairy, fast food, candy, sugar, etc. But LB was stuck in all that same ol' bullshit I desired not to offer my son, and because of that we argued like cats and dogs over virtually everything concerning him and his well-being. As a result, our constant arguing became a normal part of his existence but it never, ever seemed to bother him. In fact, he laughed watching us go at it, which was great for him because in many cases children become traumatized by that sort of thing.

It seemed like the more I enjoyed being a father, the more LB encouraged my moving out. She encouraged us to move out when everything was ok, but encouraged me to move out whenever she was angry or discontented. She hadn't pursued the divorce since serving me and claimed she only did it to get my attention. Initially, I told my attorney I didn't wanna pursue a counter divorce claim if LB dropped it. But once I discovered she canceled the divorce, I filed against her. So for the record, I divorced her. I led her to believe we were moving out so I could store all my new furniture for my apartment at our house. I bought some nice shit too--leather couches, a big screen TV, glass tables. Trust me, I was about to have the baddest single's pad ever known to mankind!

I attempted to locate an apartment real close to LB's house so I could be near my son. I got the assistance of a friend I'd previously had a romantic interlude with a few years prior. She lived in a real upscale area of town right near me and encouraged me to look for apartments in her area. I searched for a few weeks and finally found an apartment in the very same building where she resided, which was good for me because it gave me a support system. Keep in mind I'd never had a place of my own before, so the thought of having a nearby friend would be wonderful! Now everything was in place--I had the apartment, all my furniture and plenty money saved. The only thing I needed was the heart to leave my son, because I didn't want to desert my son like my grandfather deserted my dad or like my dad deserted me. I didn't wanna raise my son from another household like my grandfather did. Don't get me wrong, I was very grateful for my grandfather's efforts, but I wanted to raise my son in my home.

I didn't know what was more intense: the desire to have peace of mind away from LB, my desire to be single again or the anxiety of leaving my five-month old son. LB offered me some needed motivation to leave. It seemed like the last 30 days leading up to my departure were the worst 30 days of our entire marriage! LB argued, cursed, fought and fussed every single day! It reminded me of the saying, "It's always darkest just before the dawn." Well let me tell you, this was darker than a thousand midnights (Lol!).

LB's violent fits of rage increased as well as my arguments with her sister. It was a very ugly situation. At one point, one of their down-south, country hick-town uncles called himself threatening me over the phone. This clown gon' say, "Nah, ya don't wont me ta cum up der wit' my nine, do ya?" I told that country-ass bastard to bring his monkey-ass on. "Niggah you ain't the only one with a gun. I'll meet your bitch-ass at the city limits you telephone-gangster ass-muthafucka! You talking shit over the phone, but bring YO' ASS, niggah! Bring yo' ASS!" Ooh, I was HOT! With all the hell I was going through, he had the nerve to call there talkin' SHIT!? He was doin' a whole lotta wolfin' over the phone. But I see he kept his 'bama, country-ass where he was.

The final straw took place in the kitchen. I was trying my very best not to argue with LB, but she was in rare form that day. I'd just warmed up a plate of spaghetti which I had in my right hand, and I was holding my son in my left arm. LB was arguing about something insignificant and because I was so nonchalant about it, she smacked the plate of spaghetti outta my hand. He and I both looked to the floor as the plate broke and the spaghetti splattered. Then, she swung at me! But, I blocked her punch with my right arm, which caused my son to wobble slightly in my other arm. When that happened, we simultaneously looked at each other as we did at his birth. A thousand things went through my mind in that split second: my parents fighting, losing A.L.E., my fucked-up marriage, too much stress, too many arguments and disappointments. But mostly, I thought about how I never wanted my son to witness the domestic violence I was subjected to. In fact, as we gazed into each others eyes I told him, "Son, I guarantee you will never, ever witness anything like this again." He looked at me as if he understood and I moved out that weekend.

Let the Games Begin!

There were a few attractive women who were employed at the 24-hour drug store where I worked part time. Besides the extra money, they were definitely a fringe benefit of working there. I'd never thought twice about getting involved with any of 'em, mostly because I was married. I used to talk a little shit. You know, harmless flirting, but that's about it. But in the weeks leading up to my separation, I started dropping off a co-worker who lived nearby me. Her name was Mya... and she was cool as hell. She was so down to earth and had a wonderful, spicy little personality with a slight tomboy flavor. I could tell she had at least one brother because she seemed to know how to get along with guys. I laughed and joked with her a lot, which was very refreshing considering all the hell I was going through with LB.

Mya was mixed with Moor (black) and Egyptian, which made her looks very exotic. Her lips were thin and shaped to look like she was always frowning, but she had a beautiful smile with perfect teeth. Her breasts were her most notable external quality. Now, I don't know breast sizes, but she was bigger than two volleyballs... and they were real too. She was about 5'3" and built straight up and down... her waist was as wide as her hips. Her ass was kind of a square-ass, but it was full. She had a real sensual look in her eyes... like she could really put something on a man, if you know what I mean.

Mya was one of the first women I befriended after LB. Until then, I hadn't realized I could be friends with women. As far as I was concerned, women were for a love interest, to fuck around with or fuck over, all of which were for my personal benefit and entertainment.

Mya and I used to talk like real friends do, about regular everyday stuff... without arguing. I was never able to talk to LB like that without controversy or arguing. I was always guarded talking to LB, trying to watch out for her angle, hidden motive and agenda... but not with Mya. She had a real cool younger brother who was crazy about me. He worked down the street from us at Wendy's. So, I started taking them both home, then eventually, picking them both up for work. And, whenever we were together, we always had fun. I met her entire family, who all seemed to like me... a lot, in spite of the fact that she told them I was still married. After a while, I could tell that Mya was really, very taken with me. She said her mom and sister thought I was real sexy and told her to be careful because they could feel our attraction for each other. Shit, her brother was encouraging us to get together.

Mya made me feel wanted, like a friend... and desired in a sensual way. She made me feel special... and I've always been quite partial to being treated special. It felt like she really liked me! You know, my personality, sense of humor, my idiosyncrasies, which I considered ideal since I was longing for the love and affection only an authentic friendship could offer. But, what really endeared her to me was that she never judged me. She knew I was still married and even though we hadn't been intimate, we could feel that deep passion between us... and it felt so good and sexy. You know that sensual feeling deep down in the pit of your stomach? Yeah, we had real good chemistry and our relationship made me feel secure. I used to tell her some of the shit I was going through with LB and she would empathize with me. On several occasions, she called LB a damn fool. "You mean to tell me you pay all the bills, buy her clothes, work three jobs and go to school full time and she can't do no better than that?! Yeah, she's a damn fool!" Mya wasn't just a yes woman either. She'd tell me when and where I was wrong but she did it in a loving way, not judgmentally and because of that, I listened. Hell, I knew when I was wrong anyway.

Eventually, I knew Mya and I were going to express our passions. It was inevitable and I was wrestling with my morality. But even deep within the madness of my own religiosity, I reasoned... divorce is merely a funeral ceremony to an already dead marriage. So though I wasn't divorced yet, but only separated and looking to move out real soon, one thing was for certain... I was never going back to LB because our marriage was surely dead! So, would a sexual encounter with Mya be considered adultery?

116

Not in my rationale. Besides that, having sex as a single man was still considered sinful by virtue of fornication. So, I guess you could say I was fucked either way.

Mya had an apartment in the same neighborhood I was looking to move into. She asked me in one day as I dropped her off. We both kinda sensed something was gonna happen. I'd had sex twice in the previous six months and once since my five month old son was born, and since I didn't believe in masturbation, I had some real pinned-up sexual emotion. But, I almost felt like I owed it to Mya for showing me love and kindness at a time when I really needed it most. Plus, as I stated earlier, Mya's breasts were bigger than volleyballs and I was kinda curious to see 'em.

When we entered her apartment her roommate was there and seemed genuinely happy to meet me...like she'd heard a lot about me. She continuously looked me over and smiled a lot, like she was recollecting Mya's descriptions of me. And she was extra nice, like she'd already decided to like me because Mya liked me. Then she spontaneously hurried to leave as if Mya had prompted her to, or as if it had been prearranged. Once her roommate left my heart palpitated because I was excited and nervous, but it felt so sexy! The shades were pulled down all over the apartment, which made it dark and cool, but it accentuated the mood. It made it seem like we were sneaking...which oftentimes heightens the experience. We sat in her living room talking with the T.V. on for a while. But after a short time a sensual feeling of passion became thick in our midst. It was pure... wholesome...attraction derived from good chemistry.

Without prompting we simultaneously got up and walked in her bedroom where she closed the door, "Just in case my roommate comes back," validating her precautionary measure. She slowly walked toward me with a vampire-look in her eyes...and I loved it! She started unbuttoning my shirt while kissing me with her soft lips. She used a lot of tongue when she kissed to compensate for her thin lips, but she did her thang. The one thing I disliked about Mya was that she smoked cigarettes and I could smell a light hint of nicotine on her breath. But that wasn't gonna stop what was about to happen, so I fought through it. She slowly, softly kissed my neck with passionate bites becoming harder and harder. I had to tell her, "Hey babe, I can't go home with passion marks on my neck. I haven't moved yet." She momentarily ceased but I had to repeat it about 30 times over the next few hours.

Once she took my shirt off, she moaned and started kissing my chest like she approved of what she saw. I never gave her the location of my "G" spot, but she damn-sure found it and quick! She started nibbling on my nipples (that's one of the sexiest feelings in the world) and I was rendered utterly helpless. She started undoing my pants until I stopped her, "Hold on nah, I wanna see something too. When are you gon' take somethin' off?" "Shut up niggah, I'm doin' this!" Then she unbuckled my pants, but my erection kept my pants from falling to the floor. When she saw that, she cracked up laughing, "Hell yeah! Now that's what I'm talking about!" Then she deliberately peeled my pants off and sat me down on the edge of her bed. She placed a pillow on the floor in front of me and kneeled down upon it. Then I propped my left leg on her bed, keeping my right one on the floor. She grabbed my penis with her right hand and slowly pushed my torso down on the bed with her left. I reclined as she sucked my dick...like she loved me! And she was doing it so damn passionately too! She grunted and moaned like she was eating a slab of ribs. Hearing her enjoy herself like that made me wanna cum. Shit, she was sucking it so exquisitely I had to sit up to see what the fuck she was doin'. She made me wanna say something. I never talked during sex because I considered it unmanly and very un-playa-like. But it was feeling so damn good I didn't care. I had to let it out, "Ooooh babyyy! Yessssss! Stay right there... just like that baby, yeah, just like that!" And all the while I voiced my pleasure, she voiced her approval of it...as she continued sucking. "Mmm-hm... mmm-hm!" When I was just about to release, I tried to withdraw from her mouth, but she went deeper...massaging her tonsils. And as I came... she swallowed.

My eye's bucked out my head because she was the first woman who swallowed without having that look of disgust on her face, you know, the one people have while swallowing cod liver oil. Yeah, I was surprised because I knew Mya wasn't fucking around with anybody and she didn't have a boyfriend. In fact, her brother told me their family was glad she finally met someone she liked because she was so damn picky. So when she swallowed, it either meant she was very careless, or that she really liked and trusted me. And since I'd already received her personal tendencies and current status from her family, I knew she really liked me... a lot. The look on her face was like she'd swallowed some warm honey. She did it with a smile. That was so psychologically bonding to me. I felt an, "I love you" in the pit of my stomach, but I suppressed it from surfacing because I figured it was just a combination of repressed sexual emotion... and some damn good head.

Then she stood up, "Now, you can see something." She pulled her shirt off over her head while I sat on the bed watching her undress. To this very day, I have never seen titties that damn big... real or fake. They were so heavy she had two deep imprints on the top of her shoulders where her bra strap was embedded in her skin. When she unclamped her bra clasps behind her, it sounded like pressurized bottles of hot beer being opened. And with each clasp she unclamped, her bra jerked like it was about to fly off. Each time she unclamped one, she snickered in a sexy way, slowly shaking her head left to right like I had absolutely no idea what I was about to endeavor.

When she unclamped the last one, her bra jumped forward (and I almost ducked). She started laughing at my facial expression because I was in awe! She sat down on the bed and I fondled them like new gold bars. I eased her back onto the bed and the weight of her breasts pushed her down. They covered her entire upper body. They were big, wide, stout, firm, full and heavy! "Goddamn girl, what the hell am I supposed to do with these!?" And I was serious too. Her nipples were so big I struggled to get one in my mouth and when I did, it was damn near too big to suck. It was like trying to suck on the tip of a pickle. She laughed so hard, watching me struggle with her breasts that tears came to her eyes. "Don't worry baby, I got something you can deal with." Then she reached over and grabbed a condom off her nightstand and gave it to me. As I put it on she peeled her tight-fitting, soaking wet panties off, opened her legs and motioned with her finger for me to come and lie on top of her. Now this was what life was all about! Fellas', remember in the movie The Best Man when Terrence Howard's character delivers the line, "Ain't nothin better than pussy, but some new pussy?" Was that the truth or what? I love that rush I get seconds before entering a woman. It feels like Christmas morning with a hundred presents under the tree... like walking into a smorgasbord restaurant after starving all day long... like a big, cold pitcher of water while working in the hot sun.

She was the first woman who ever inserted my dick into her. Now that was some real sexy shit right there! It was so feminine, and yet, assertive at the same time. She set a standard with that one. It was similar to when the Moor (black) girl unlocked the car door for the character "C" in the movie A Bronx Tale. It was so considerate! Besides men can't see down there anyway...so we need all the help we can get and I appreciated her assistance. Fellas'! Have you ever taken that first stroke and realized she was about to make your fave five list? First of all, under normal circumstances condoms subdue sexual stimulation, but Mya's pussy was so snug, warm and inviting, (WHOO!) her energy penetrated the latex. Secondly, we caught our rhythm on the very first stroke...as I eased in she simultaneously slid herself upon me. And as I slowly...and very passionately...made perfect circles with my hips, Mya mimicked my very same motions...like vast, smooth waves upon the oceans. We shared the same sensuous rhythm...in the pushin' of our passion we were both feelin' and givin'. I looked down and saw Mya's hips coming all the way off the bed with every stroke. It was then I realized we weren't just fucking... we were making love.

Makin' Love

To me, making love is strictly about the passion.

It's about the oohs and the ahhs.

It's about the scents and the tears.

It's about that look on her face... that it hurts so good!

It's about releasing all your fears.

It's about being totally uninhibited...

No limits... no boundaries...

It's about fulfilling her deepest desire and your sensual fantasy.

It's about allowing her femininity to accentuate the most masculine man in me.

It's about the love and admiration... respect and trust... care and concern...

It's totally mental... extremely sentimental... as we both teach and learn.

Envisioning her in my mind as I see her in my eyes... a double take, the mental picture of her physical being.

It's about totally emptying yourself on her, in her.

It's about flowing all through her and offering her your everything.

As we made love, tears ran down the corners of her eyes onto her pillow. I'll have to admit, up to that point in my life I'd never, ever made love before... not like this. After a while our love-making became spiritual, and every few minutes she'd make this sound like she was descending into a scalding hot tub of water and blurted out her thoughts like she had turrets syndrome , "Tssssss, uuuhhh... your wife is a Goddamn fool... and you can tell her I said it!" Then we both laughed. Her pc muscles were offering all the loving constriction, and I could hardly stand it. The more she constricted, the more I expanded, to the point of us busting the condom. But later, after we busted the second condom, we just kept going because we were slowly approaching an overwhelming climax... together. Mya released a long, sensuous moan as she clamped her vaginal walls upon me, but we never stopped our rhythm. I basked in her cry of ecstasy and after she composed herself, I asked her to turn over and she got on her hands and knees. She was just as fulfilling from that position and every other position we attempted that afternoon. And just before my big release, she whispered to me, "You don't have to take it out when you cum." And I was like... "Why not?" "It's alright...you don't have to." "Really, are you on birth control?" "Uhhh, no...I just know my body. Just trust me, its O.K." Usually when a woman says trust me in that situation...I don't! No offense against

Mya, but self-preservation was most important, so I withdrew anyway.

Fellas! Why does our orgasm become more intense when there's a chance she can get pregnant? I felt my orgasm start in the base of my neck, then it descended down through my spine and by the time it came through my testicles and surfaced through my shaft, she was putting it on me like nobody's business. Just before I released she pulled out, turned around, and placed me deep in her mouth. I released a long, slow moan of ecstasy that probably disturbed the neighbors... six months of pinned-up emotion, three years of bad marriage, tension and stress was released... when I released. It felt like a string of silk slowly being pulled through my penis. She did her best to swallow it all, but her eyes got big as she gagged.

When I came to (back from the journey of my orgasm), I was kneeling erect upon my knees in the middle of her bed with my head tilted back and my hands upon the back of her shoulders. I was shaking like I had Parkinson's from over-stimulation. I looked down at her as she looked up at me with her expression of the 'cat that swallowed the canary.' She knew my whole genital area was extra sensitive from over-stimulation, so I gently asked her to let me go because we both knew what was coming next.

Ladies! Why is it when men finish orgasming, y'all like playing with our penises, knowing damn well it's extra sensitive? You could give a man a fuckin' heart attack doing that!

She kept moving her tongue and lips around as I screamed like a lil' girl. "Stop playin' Mya, let me go, don't do that... Ohhh shit, stop playin'!" She was crying tears laughing at me, but she did it while maintaining her lip-tight seal around my penis. When she finally released me, she wrestled me down and we engaged in the most loving after play I'd ever experienced. Afterward, we got real comfortable and started drifting off to sleep. That was my cue that it was time to leave. Besides, I had to hurry home to take a shower before LB got home from work. Mya kissed me several times with such passion before she let me out.

Upon arriving home I took a long, hot bath, attempting to wash Mya's scent off my body. But more accurately, to deliberate over what I'd done from a moral standpoint. It seemed like my conscious kicked in directly after I released. Before that, making love to Mya was the closest thing to Heaven I'd ever experienced. I didn't feel sorry or bad for cheating on LB because I only considered it cheating if I were gonna stay married to her, which was definitely not the case. My primary focus was moving out so I could sincerely enjoy my single life without LB having a legitimate complaint of infidelity.

I visited Mya again that same week and the intensity of our love making multiplied. We even made love while her roommate was there, and trying to keep quiet only heightened the intensity. In time, I started to notice Mya becoming more emotional. She wanted more foreplay and after play, during which time she'd verbalize her sentiments... which bothered me. "I think we'd make a great couple; I know I could make you happy. You'd always have a hot meal every night, and I can cook my ass off, too. Are you moving in a two bedroom? Dayum, I can't wait till I can spend the night at your place." Now mind you, we'd never discussed any of those things before... ever! It made me feel so uncomfortable that it turned me off. In fact, her brother started calling me brother-in law, which used to irritate the shit outta me. A couple of times I told her, "Look Mya, I'm not even divorced yet and you're talking about marriage. Honey, it's gonna take some time to rediscover myself before I can jump into another serious relationship. She listened intently, but she never really heard me. I started to feel bad for her because she was really in love... but I wasn't.

I knew I had to call it quits with Mya because she had that look of love in her eyes that I didn't share. Her family was being just too nice to me. Her brother started wanting to hang out with me all the time. It was like she and her entire family was forcing marriage upon me... even before I got divorced. Mya even got to the point where she wanted to beat up LB solely based upon some of the stuff I told her. "Just give me the word and I'll fuck that crazy bitch up!" I actually had to stop telling her what was going on. I guess she was too emotionally involved to realize that regardless, LB was the mother of my son and for that alone, I would always have a realm of care and concern for her well-being.

One night my supervisor (where Mya and I worked) asked me into his office. By that time he and I had become best friends and were as close as brothers. I'd invited him to my church where he became a member and some years later, a minister. I even made him my son's godfather. I rarely befriend males, but when I do, we become closer than brothers. My supervisor Crenshow was no exception. He was about 5'7" and over 400 pounds with extremely broad shoulders, big hands and size 14 Double E feet. He played high school football so he was the biggest little guy I ever knew. He also had one of the biggest hearts a man could have and rarely ever got angry. But when he did, it was never for long. He was extremely dedicated and committed to whatever he endeavored, so he often sacrificed himself for the sake of his occupational position. He always looked out for me by offering me the precise days and hours I requested to work. Crenshow didn't have a driver's license, so I made it my duty to get him to and from work, whether I worked or not. It was a labor of love for me because for all practical purposes he was my brother. Often times I'd take him, Mya and her brother home together. But he never suspected anything between Mya and me...until the day he asked me into his office.

"Hey man, what's going on between you and Mya?" And of course, I gave him the deer in the headlights expression. "What chu talkin' 'bout Show?" Then a smile came over my face that I couldn't contain as I broke out into laughter. "Man, I have no idea what you're talking about." By that time, he was laughing too, "Yeah, I can tell by the way you're laughing... come on man, spill the beans." "Why are you asking me that, Show?" "Man, you know me and Mya been cool for a while, even before you started taking her home and we're kinda close. The other day we were laughing about something silly you did and she told me she really liked you and thought you were a good man." "So, what's wrong with that? I like her too, she's cool. Like a lil' sister."

Crenshow chuckled, "Oh for real, a lil' sista huh? Well, I think there's some incest goin' on, 'cause she just broke out boo-hooin' outta nowhere and when I asked her what was wrong, she just said nothing and walked away. Now, Mya usually tells me everything... so what's going on between y'all?"

"Show, man... I done messed around and hit it." "What!? You lying! I knew somethin' was up. You'da MAN, Doc! So how was them titties?" "Show, you know I don't kiss and tell." "Negro please, you better talk to me before I fire you." Then we both fell out laughing. "Oh my GOD Show, I've never seen anything like it." "And, how was the pussy... did she have the snapper?" "Yes sah!" Crenshow and I had talked about that sensual look in Mya's eyes before. "Its official Doc, she's definitely got the snapper!" "Man that girl's in love with you, it's all over her face... so what you gon' do now, does LB know?" "Nope, but I need to break it off because she's already talkin' 'bout marriage." "Marriage!? Man, you ain't even divorced yet. Ooh-wee, you got problems brah...was it worth it?" I thought for a minute. "Well, it depends on how this all turns out, then I can answer that question."

I'd decided to at least wait until I moved to my new apartment before entertaining company again. It was the proper thing to do. And though Mya was an exquisite lover, it was easy for me to stop because my moral conscious was still active. Meanwhile, as the weekend approached, I had Crenshow and another guy we worked with who owned a truck help me move to my new apartment. We did it in the late evening and by the time we finished, it was late night. They loved my place and Crenshow was so happy for me because he knew all the shit I was going through with LB and was happy I was finally away from it all. After they left I remember getting on my knees in the living room, kissing the carpet and thanking GOD for peace of mind. In fact, I just laid on my back and stared at the ceiling until I drifted off to sleep. I woke up the next day smack dab in the middle of my living room floor... and it was the most restful sleep I'd had in over three years.

Full Speed Ahead

My apartment was beautiful, warm and inviting. I had two bedrooms, but used one as a den. My master bedroom was enormous. My friend who lived in the apartment complex told me her job was selling their old office furniture, so I bought an executive-sized desk and a five-drawer file cabinet to go in my bedroom. I had a queen-sized bed with a huge double mirror dresser and a cedar closet and still had so much room to spare. I was so excited because though I'd been married, this was the first time I'd ever been on my own... and I loved it. I was always buying things for my new place. And though I didn't have a housewarming party, people bought a lot of things for me. I wanted to fully express myself within my décor. I did it all for my own comfort and convenience and to obtain the approval of everyone that visited. I loved receiving compliments, "I just love your place. This is really nice." And if they didn't immediately complement my place, I'd always fish for compliments. "Yeah, I just moved in so I gotta fix the place up." "Fix the place up? It's beautiful like you have it." Then I was satisfied.

I decided to have the utmost respect for my home as a place of sanctity. I've always been a very private person (that's my Piscean energy), so all visitors considered themselves privileged and fortunate. It was like the bat cave on the original Batman series; my apartment was located at the end of a small forest, which acted as a dead end. So there was only one way in and one way out. I lived in one of the most prominent communities in the city. People always had difficulty finding my place, which was good for me because it meant nobody was just gonna drop by. When people visited me, it was deliberate, and they could never use the excuse of just being in the neighborhood because most people couldn't find it without directions and two phone calls to lead them in. I decided my place wasn't going to be a whore house with women spending the night all the time. I even set my own curfew. All female company had to leave before midnight on the weekend and when they asked why, I told them because I'd turn into a werewolf after midnight.

Besides my own religiosity and practicing Christianity, I established this kind of environment for my son's sake because I wanted him to grow up around positive energy. Whenever I did 'the do', I always did it at the woman's place and I never allowed any woman to spend the night at my apartment. When I spent the night with a woman, it was always at her house... at least in the beginning. The most important thing to me was my son. LB brought him over every day after I got off work. I fixed a four-course dinner at least three times a week because I never wanted my son to eat fast food, junk food or anything of the like. Besides, I loved cooking and it was also a draw card for women. They loved the fact that I was a great cook and prepared a meal daily. I always told women not to call or come by until after eight when LB picked up my son. I always wanted the time with my son to be uninterrupted. But of course there were always some hard-headed women who refused to follow instructions who'd end up coming by before eight, observing me interacting with my son...which was another attraction for women.

Beam Me Up Scotty

Shortly after moving to my apartment, I lost contact with Mya. She found another job and moved away. I interpreted that as divine intervention because eventually, I was just going to double back and continue what we'd started. But Mya's departure only paved the way for another woman who worked with us. Her name was Monay, but I called her Moonbeam because she was so damn flighty. She had a short Jeri Curl (which even back in the early 90's was a little outdated) with a cute little round face and a wide smile like Whoopi Goldberg. Her eyes would light up whenever she laughed. Moonbeam was loud as hell and spoke with a slow southern drawl. She was a size 6 who stood about 5'6", slim and well-proportioned with a plump lil' ass.

She was my manicurist while I was married and was extremely professional. She did the manicures at her mother's house, I guess because she didn't want to disclose the location of her own place. And she was very careful not to appear inappropriate or forward. She conducted herself in ladylike fashion and made sure I knew she respected my marital situation. I maintained a very professional relationship with her during my manicures, but we were cordially casual at work where she appeared more uptight. Moonbeam was very religious, or at least she went to church a lot, but through all of her posturing, I could still tell she liked me. She only charged me four dollars for a full manicure, claiming that was my discounted price because we worked together. It took her an hour to do the job... and I thought that was a pretty low price for so much work; it wasn't even minimum wage back in the early 90s so she might as well have done it for free... but that would've tipped her hand. I think she enjoyed the opportunity of getting to know me better. She'd seen LB once or twice at the store and commented, "Yo' wife is very pretty."

I remember gazing upon Moonbeam's face as she did my nails. She had a perfect complexion and appeared to have good hygiene, which has always been a major attraction for me. It took me a few months before realizing she always scheduled my appointments around our paydays... when she could touch up her Jeri Curl. She was trying to look her best for our appointments because she realized I was checking her out while she performed her services. Every now and then she'd look up at me, gazing at her, and offer a shy smile. But during and after my separation, I used to gaze at her while daydreaming about us fucking. But the strange thing was she'd look at me with a sensual smirk and her eyebrow raised like she knew what I was thinking.

After my separation, I used to kick myself in the ass after every manicure appointment because I wanted to initiate something between Moonbeam and me, but I was too apprehensive. Often times, my manicure got damaged working at my full time job because it was so hands-on. But, I really started going twice a week as an excuse to see Moonbeam more outside of work. By then she was doing them at her apartment and charging me four dollars every other visit. Once she discovered I was separated, she started doing my manicures for free. "I saw yo' wife in the store wit' cho' son the other day... he's so cute... y'all got a beautiful family. I asked her if she was lookin' for you. But she just looked at me strange and asked if she could use yo' discount." When Moonbeam told me that I was pissed, because my sentiment was when I leave you... so do all of my benefits. "Hey Monay don't give her my discount anymore... we're separated and soon to be divorced. I'll make sure I tell Crenshow so he can inform all the other staff." "Oh, I'm sooorry to hear that, I didn't know. No wonder she looked at me so funny." "Naw, don't be sorry, shit, I'm not." Then we both laughed. Yeah, Moonbeam might've said she was sorry to hear about my separation, but her facial expression looked like she'd just hit the lottery. I guess from then on, we knew it was only a matter of time.

Although I knew Moonbeam and I would soon share intimacies, I still felt dissatisfied coming home that night alone. It had been a few months since being with Mya and I was feeling vulnerable. Nobody ever briefed me on what it's like being separated. It was different. I mean, I had the peace of mind I so desperately wanted and needed. But I really, really missed being away from my son. LB brought him over every day, but she never allowed him to spend the night. Her excuse was that he was still too young. But that was just one of the things she did to try to control me. I really missed just watching my son in his crib and being there observing his growth and maturity from day to day.

During this time, I discovered energies. You see, a person creates his own energy within his environment. When LB and I were together, there was an intense, anxious energy in our home. When I lived at home with my mom, there was a 'you're-no-longer-welcomed-here-so-get-your-monkey-ass-out energy.' So, I sought to create my own unique and special energy within my apartment, first and foremost, by always keeping it immaculate. I also read and studied the bible religiously, not to mention attending church all day Sunday, choir rehearsal on Tuesdays and bible study on Wednesdays. So there was a very calm, serene, sacred energy in my apartment. Everyone felt it when they visited and that's probably why almost everybody fell asleep at my place. Music is also an energy I utilized. I've always loved music, so either my stereo or the television was always playing, which made it feel like another person was there. I played a little rap, some gospel and a lot of jazz. Back then, George Duke had a real hot joint called "Geneva" on his Snapshot CD. Also, "No Rhyme No Reason," featuring Rachelle Ferrell. Speaking of which, I sho' nuff wore her CD out. She was the only woman I would've married back then. "Till You Come Back to Me" still brings tears to my eyes whenever I hear it because that goddess sings from the depths of her very soul. I used to imagine LB singing that to me, then I'd chuckle because it damn sure was never gonna happen.

But with regard to separation, nobody ever told me how loud the silent walls were, or about getting used to sleeping alone again. Don't misunderstand me, I was glad to be away from LB but it was just a total readjustment, learning how to be single again. The weekends were more difficult because I didn't do the club scene and I was trying to live right, according to Christian standards and biblical principles. It became increasingly frustrating attending churches populated with 80% women. That's why I was so frustrated returning home from Moonbeam's manicures; I was more so desiring to feel loved than I was horny. A week later, I went to our regularly scheduled appointment a little sharper, wearing a little more cologne and sporting a fresh haircut. I also purchased a three pack of condoms...just in case. We talked more that evening than we ever had before. Moonbeam laughed and smiled a lot that night and was a lot more comfortable too. She took a little longer than usual to finish my manicure. It seemed like she was giving me the opportunity to make my move.

Once she finished and I was about to leave her apartment, all I could think about was being at home alone, wishing I'd had the courage to proposition her. As we slowly strolled to the elevator, even Moonbeam appeared subtly disappointed. I made some small conversation while we waited for the elevator... that's when I initiated my attempt. "Monay, can you keep a secret?" She looked at me with subtle anticipation. "Yeah, I can." "Are you sure?" "Uh-huh, I'm sure." I motioned for her to come closer with my finger. As I stepped forward peering into her eyes, our heads tilted opposite ways because it was abundantly clear we were about to kiss. It happened so fast... but in slow motion all at the same time. [I can't express how I love and live for those moments]. We were only a step away from each other, but she stepped forward before I could complete my step. I'd planned to kiss her, but she ended up kissing me. Just before our lips embraced, I saw her nervous, anxious expression that was both feminine and vulnerable. She kissed me like she'd just been released from a five-year prison bid. Yeah, I could tell she wanted that kiss for a long, long time. She kept shrilling in this sexy, high-pitched tone like she was both overwhelmed and over stimulated, and I could feel the vibration of her shrilling in my mouth as we kissed... and that was so sensual.

Our first kiss lasted for what seemed like an hour. She'd placed her

130

hands behind my head while mine were respectfully on the small of her back. When we broke apart, it was like resurfacing from a deep water dive. We were panting in rhythm and apparently amazed by our true passions for each other. The elevator was an intrusion as it arrived. Moonbeam grabbed my hand and led me back into her apartment. Then she closed and locked the door. We kissed each other with the energy of a whirlwind twisting toward her daybed. I was so shocked at how she was taking the lead in our endeavor. She started removing her clothes. I felt around my pockets for the condoms, but realized I'd left them in the car. I decided not to bring them in so I wouldn't be mistaken for being presumptuous.

When I saw her taking off her clothes, I didn't wanna be rude so I followed suit (Lol!). Her eyes were so wide open and focused upon me, it was extremely apparent she wanted it as much as I did... or more. She asked me if I had protection and I told her it was in the car. She exhaled in exasperation, "In the car? Ba-by!!! Did you wanna go and get 'em?" She lived on the third floor. Plus, it was hard as hell working that slow-ass, old-styled, cast-iron elevator. In other words, I was too lazy and over-anxious to get the condoms from my car. "Girl, I'm not goin' out there now! I guess we won't be able to do that tonight... but I got something else we can do." Moonbeam always appeared to be hygienically correct, which was a turn on. So, I wanted to see just how clean she really was. I laid her on the daybed and started sucking her titties. She was already hot, but I was heating up the fire. I kissed near all the important places: her arm pits, her ass, and her feet...she was immaculate! Not only was she clean, I surmised she'd bathed before our appointment. My foot fetish got the best of me and I sucked her toes. She loved every second of it... but not as much as I did.

Once I was satisfied about her hygiene, I went for her *honeycomb*. Moonbeam was the first woman I tasted after separating from LB and I was hungry for it too. She was palming the back of my head with such a passionate grip, I got the notion she either hadn't been tasted before, or hadn't been tasted properly. It must've been her secret fantasy, because her reactions and responses came from deep within her soul, "That's it... YESSS... that's it!" Then, she chuckled. I looked up and her eyes were closed, but she was grinning from ear to ear. Moonbeam was in heaven. Her clitoris was rapidly pulsating between my lips as I slowly flicked my tongue against it. I knew she was about to cum so I flipped my tongue faster to match her clitoral pulsations. She was kinda loud, but I didn't care because I didn't live there.

When Moonbeam had her orgasm, she damn near broke my neck. She pushed my head back with both hands because she couldn't fully embrace the high intensity of her orgasm. When I heard my neck snap, crackle and pop, I grabbed her arms and interlocked them with mine. Then she tried to squirm away from me, so I positioned myself where she couldn't escape. I could tell by her reactions that an orgasm of such intensity was a completely new experience for her... and I was determined to guide her through the complete experience. Damn, she was strong as hell. I mean, I really had to pin her down. Once I felt her warm surge of cum upon my lips, I licked her clit softer, slower and more passionately. That's when she started screaming bloody murder. I thought one of her neighbors was gonna call the police... but oooh, she tasted so sweet!

It took Moonbeam about 5 minutes to regain her composure. She looked at me like she'd been electrocuted. Her eyes were so wide open. Then, she started laughing, which made them even wider. She'd had a taste of the appetizer, but her facial expression read that she was now ready for the main course (which was my entrée). That's when the deliberations began: "Well, I'm O.K. I haven't been wit' anyone since I broke up wit' my boyfriend eight months ago, and I stopped havin' sex with him about two months before we broke up because I didn't trust him. Then I took an AIDS test after we broke up." For whatever reason, I believed her. Then she looked at me, because it was my turn. But I wanted the pussy so bad, I gotta admit the truth... I lied, "Well, as you know, I'm separated from my wife and you'll be the only woman I've been with, besides her, in four and a half years."

Moonbeam's eyes watered a little as she hung onto my every word and slowly shook her head in approval of being the first after my separation. I guess she felt special. "We took a mandatory test before we got married and neither of us has ever messed around." She was ready to believe my truth before I'd finished lying. Condom or not, it was on. I was sitting back on her daybed buck-naked with an erection harder than Chinese Trigonometry when she straddled me. We kissed and gnawed each other until she finally sat on my dick, and even though she was real wet, there was so much resistance getting in. It substantiated her account of not having sex for the previous ten months. I mean, she was real tight, like a virgin. But she wiggled, grinded, and worked her way down on it.

She moaned and grunted with every twist and turn, and more than halfway down I knew it was going to be a wonderful encounter because I could feel the back of her. She obviously felt it too because she started cursing, "Oh shit, oh shit, ahhhh-ssiiii... push it all the way in baby!" I figured she was kinda masochistic because I was already all the way in and couldn't go any further. While I was passionately pushing pleasure in her private part, Moonbeam grabbed the top rail behind me and continuously pulled herself further onto me (like she was rowing a boat), and then she hooked her feet behind the bottom rail for additional leverage. I had no idea she was like this! It felt like I was in her stomach, but since she was obviously enjoying herself (in such a very loud way), I wasn't hurting her as I'd initially suspected. My dick was so hard I couldn't even feel it anymore, but it didn't matter because she certainly could. Moonbeam was now (also) one of my fave five. I mean, her pussy was so tight and wet it was surreal; unrealistic, like a fantasy that I never wanted to end. Mya may have had more passion, but Moonbeam was so much more erotic. It's hard to say what's better--passion or erotica--but we fucked in every position our young minds could imagine.

As much as I relished the passionate expression of sexual intercourse, I had a terrible dilemma. I hated coming (and still do) because it always ignited my guilty conscious. I knew it was inevitable that after expressing myself with such great passion for an extended period with Moonbeam, I was due to release. I'd practice celibacy for months at a time, but as I stated earlier, suppressing a natural human function usually promotes a corresponding perversion. So that night, I did something for the first time. I withheld. I let Moonbeam cum as often as she wanted and I took one for the team. But my conscious was all the better for it.

I spent the night at Moonbeam's and slept like a baby. I guess being cuddled up next to a warm beauty makes all the difference, even if it's just for a night. She woke up the next morning looking so happy, but I wasn't feeling all that lovey-dovey bullshit (I was kinda cranky because I didn't cum). Plus, I used to feel so convicted leaving a woman's house in the morning. It felt sinful and it always seemed like someone was watching me. The guilt was twice as strong leaving on Sunday mornings. Then, I felt like shit all day in church...asking GOD for forgiveness, especially when I knew I was gonna do the same shit, sooner or later. Religion really does a mind job on the human psyche. I once read that a constant state of conviction is the unhealthiest condition in the human experience because it constricts the mind and kills the body slowly like a cancer. All religions with their corresponding sins and thou-shalt-nots are exclusively credited with perpetuating that state of conviction. I discovered the recipe for sharing my intimate passions without the corresponding conviction and guilty conscious--more tasting and avoid cumming.

Moonbeam was so sweet to me and seemed to be the marrying kind. She was very monogamous with a very high sense of fidelity, clean, kind, loving... and she definitely wanted a relationship. But honestly, I didn't consider Moonbeam a serious potential consideration even if I was in the right situation because she was too flighty. She was cute, but not quite cute enough to represent me. She had a tiny little apartment and her full-time job was working in a drug store. She was beneath me and wasn't my personal idea of a keeper. I had much greater expectations in a keeper than that. Plus, she was about three or four years too early anyway.

Moonbeam, like Mya, obviously saw something very husband-like in me because, she too, immediately began trying to cultivate a serious relationship (Damn!). Neither of them seemed to realize or care that I wasn't even divorced yet. Nor did they assume I'd need some additional time to myself before jumping into another serious relationship. Otherwise, it would've been unfair to them because I'd just be on the rebound. Our second sexual encounter was a tremendous letdown from the first. I guess she had to get the monkey off her back on our first encounter since she hadn't had any for ten months prior. Moonbeam tried to make me offer her a verbal agreement to have a serious relationship. Suddenly her religiosity surfaced, "I can't keep having sex without being married, but being in a committed relationship is a start." And, we had this kind of conversation directly before fucking, so unfortunately, there was nothing extraordinary about our second encounter, and I had such high expectations too. So Moonbeam dropped out of my fave five as an individual, but our initial encounter made it to my pussy hall of fame.

My Piscean energy has always made me extremely sensitive to hurting people, especially women. Besides, I'd rather tell 'em the truth and let 'em deal with it. Moonbeam made me feel claustrophobic, and three of my pet peeves are boredom, goin' 'round in circles, and feeling claustrophobic. So, I told Moonbeam she was a wonderful woman and certainly the marrying kind, but the timing was all wrong for a commitment or relationship. We stayed in touch by occasional phone calls. But it was evident that she was only looking for a permanent arrangement with me, so she wouldn't allow me to get into any compromising positions with her. She wasn't giving up the pussy, and for whatever reason, that made me desire her all the more. Here's my complexity:. when women are too affectionate or throwing the pussy at me, I feel crowded, claustrophobic or a little suspicious. But when they withhold it, it's attractive to me. I want a woman who likes me, loves me and has my back. But I can't stand when she's too needy, too clingy or becomes somewhat of a stalker. I certainly don't want a promiscuous woman, but I also don't want an uptight, sexually repressed woman. I want a morally upright woman, but not a religious fanatic. She has to be extremely passionate and erotic, but without having an extensive sexual past. It's all about balance.

The Mack Attack

I was at the apex of my thespian career in the 1990s and stumbled upon a tremendous stage production opportunity. A high school friend and fellow thespian informed me about a play audition and suggested I attend. I wasn't really interested in a stage acting opportunity, but I figured it would only fortify my thespian experience to be involved in some capacity. So, I met her there and cold read for a few different parts. The playwright then asked for my opinion on how to play a 65-year-old mortician from the deep, deep South with a comedic flavor. I did a cold reading and he was blown away, "I got my lead character right here!" The rest of the cast (who'd already secured parts) cheered and applauded my efforts because I brought so much energy to the character and the play needed a strong lead. I came to the audition for a casual involvement, but ended up getting the lead part.

Normally, I never mixed business with pleasure. No matter how gorgeous the women were, I never used to fraternize with them. I considered that tacky and since so many male thespians were straight up dogs, I never wanted to be identified with them or have that as my reputation. In fact, my reputation was absolutely spotless. I wasn't just considered a great actor, I was known as a virtuoso actor extraordinaire... and strictly professional. I took acting and my talent very seriously.

The director quickly fell in love with my on-stage character and my off-stage personality. We became very good friends overnight. Craig was a very young and charismatic producer who could talk virtually anybody into doing anything. He just had the 'gift of gab' with a strong willed personality as it related to communicating with and organizing people. The entire cast was older than him, some much older, but everyone gave him great respect. He was the writer, director and producer of his own play and I was very impressed with how sophisticated he was in his arena, especially at such a young age. And I consider myself very hard to impress. He'd previously produced a comedy show, which showcased many up and coming local comedians in and around Detroit. It was a tremendous success. The local newspapers ran a story on Craig and the success of the production. Everybody in the play had great expectations. We all felt privileged to be involved with the production and associated with Craig.

Most of the women in the play were models while most of the guys were comedians. In fact, I was the only stanch actor in the play. But everyone respected each other's abilities and expertise. There were some

136

sho' nuff fine-ass women in the play, and many more hung around the rehearsals thanks in part to one of the main characters named Darrell. He was a spokesmodel for the Auto Show and was credited for bringing all the models around. Darrell was "da man". He was about 6'3", slim and black as the ace of spade. He had an extremely magnetic personality, especially with the women. I can't lie. I gotta give the brotha his props. He was very handsome, and he knew it. All the women loved Darrell's dirty drawers. He was good-looking, intelligent, and articulate, with a great personality, and he was fun to be around. He respected my acting and singing abilities and I respected his modeling thing and his Mack. Darrell brought a different fine-ass model to each rehearsal. We rehearsed five days a week for more than eight weeks. Shit, a lot of times, the guys were anxious to come to rehearsal just to see who Darrell would bring. He was also acquainted with a lot of celebrities in the entertainment business too.

Darrell put a lot of pressure on a brotha. Seeing all those fine-ass honeys made me wanna get my Mack on. I'm not gonna say it was Darrell's fault, but seeing him do his thang made me wanna do mine. So, it was only a matter of time before I started mixing business with pleasure. I used to bring my son to some of the rehearsals, and a few times, he cried louder than our combined chatter. All of those gorgeous models took turns trying to calm him and they instantly fell in love with him which made them connect with me. I felt a few of them vibing with me, but I maintained my professionalism, which intrigued them. They were very mesmerized by my acting ability and any time I got the opportunity to showcase my vocal singing gift they were really enamored. Darrell could do a little bit of everything and was very good at many things, but he was a wanna-be singer. Once he discovered I could also croon my ass off, we became instant friends and Darrell, Craig and I became the three musketeers.

Since Darrell was the sho' nuff man, I used to defer to him. I had my own mack that was very effective, but when we were together, I played the wish-I-could-be-a-Mack-like-you-Darrell role. That seemed to really endear me to him (the ego thing works on men every time). All the guys, including myself, wanted to know if he was fucking all the women he brought to the rehearsals. So when I felt we were cool enough, I asked him. But he was so evasive and gave me that I-don't-kiss-and-tell bullshit. That was very classy on his part, but we figured he was fucking a good portion of them. Surprisingly, Darrell actually had a steady girlfriend with whom he had a serious relationship. She was cute, but nothin like some of them fine-ass models he brought to rehearsals. She rarely came to rehearsal with him. Hell, we were all shocked to know he even had a steady girlfriend. Having so many different women around you feels so good. To me, there's absolutely no better way to live.

Craig had previously mentioned the woman slated to star as my wife in the play and I became somewhat anxious to meet her, especially as he and other cast members vouched for her acting credits and how fine she was. "Brotha, I got a surprise for ya'. Just thank me later and don't ever say I didn't give you anything for ya' birthday." Then he gave his signature, contagious laugh, "She can act her butt off and she's fine too. Now tell me ya' love me." But when Marshann sauntered into her first rehearsal, I was subtly disappointed. She wasn't my type at all, not that she had to be, but it would've been good for chemistry purposes. Marshann had that retro 80s look...light-skinned with green eyes and curly hair. She was about 5'8" and extremely sultry, bordering on sexy. Her pretty face and full lips accentuated her wonderfully voluptuous size 10 frame. I figured if I was gonna start mixing business with pleasure, it definitely was not gonna be with her. She was the total opposite of what I preferred in women, at least from a physical aspect.

In my personal experience, women who looked like Marshann were most often arrogant, conceited and thought they were the shit merely based upon their light-skin tone, eye color and hair texture. Darrell already knew Marshann because she used to work with him as an Auto- Show spokes-model. But then again, he knew damn near every woman in the Detroit metropolitan area. Marshann seemed used to guys fawning all over her, which was another reason I refused to pay her tribute, or offer her any extra attention. I never mimicked what most guys did because I never wanted to be viewed as predictable. But all the cock-hounds in the play immediately started jockeying for position, which made me stand out all the more. In essence, Marshann noticed me because I ignored her.

And to be very honest, she wasn't all that good in her comedic role. I think she was more of a dramatic actor anyway. My rendition of the lead character was just too energetic for her and Craig constantly rode her back about matching my intensity and energy. I also think she felt a little overwhelmed by the large assortment of talented people in the production. You definitely had to possess sheer confidence, and 'strut yo' stuff' in that environment, or else somebody would show-out on you.

One Friday evening while Craig was running a scene with Marshann and me, he let us have it! "Cut, cut, what are y'all doing?! Y'all are not convincing as husband and wife! Y'all look like two people acting like husband and wife, and that ain't gon' fly! Y'all are excused from rehearsal. Go out to dinner or lunch or something. Spend some time together until y'all get to know each other!" Marshann and I looked at Craig like he was crazy. But he continued, "Naw I'm serious, go on and get out of here! Y'all got the whole weekend to work that out, come back and try it again on Monday! In fact let that be y'all homework assignment for this weekend... get acquainted with each other! Have a good evening!" The whole cast agreed and they all laughed us out the door. I was mad and so embarrassed, but Craig was right. The rehearsals were so fun and energetic that I hated to leave, but we respected his constructive criticism and left.

It was summertime, so at 6:45 pm the sun was still out. I really didn't feel like getting acquainted with Marshann, but I obliged for the sake of the production. She initiated the conversation, "So where you wanna go?" "Well, I ate before I came so I'm not hungry. You wanna just sit in the car and...maybe talk?" "Ok, that's cool we can sit in my car." She lowered the windows and a wonderful summer breeze settled the mood. We started out with a basic conversation and by the time we realized it was 11 o'clock, we'd been in deep conversation for over four hours. We talked as the sun went down... as the evening turned to night... as all the cast members piled out of rehearsal... and as the last people left. We actually waved to everybody as they left a few at a time, and they were all still laughing at us. But by that time, it didn't bother me any more. Craig and Darrell were the last to leave and as they got in the car, they looked at us like something extracurricular was going on. When we actually got ready to leave I was hungry, so we went and got something to eat. We had a real good time just talking and getting to know each other.

After we finished eating and running lines in the restaurant neither one of us appeared ready to part company, so I asked if she had a curfew. She said her boyfriend worked midnights so she had until 6:30 am. I suggested that we go back to my apartment and she was game. Marshann's boyfriend was 12 years older than her and during our conversation she disclosed his laid-back, passive demeanor. In contrast, she seemed to really enjoy my young, energetic personality (she was four years older than me) and contrary to what I originally perceived about her, she was actually pretty charming. In fact, as we opened up to each other, I discovered we got along quite well.

When we got to my apartment I could tell Marshann was impressed but she tried to suppress it, "Nice place. It's rare to see a man keep his place so... tidy. Your girlfriend must live here with you." That was her way of fishing for information. "First of all, that's a very sexist statement you just made. Secondly, I'm in the process of a divorce, and I live alone." Marshann and I quickly developed an oil and water duo, but we had fun with it. I always had people remove their shoes before entering my apartment to preserve my light-colored carpet. She seemed more than happy to fashion her cute little pudgy feet that were well-pedicured. She sat on my couch with her legs behind her and made herself at home without my suggestion. I always kept a bottle of wine on hand so I popped the cork as we ran lines, talked and joked with each other. Marshann stayed to 6:40 that morning and acted like she didn't wanna leave then. We'd talked all night long and were officially well-acquainted.

I'd been in my apartment a couple of months and by this time, Angel (my friend who initially helped me find the apartment) and I had become playmates. I met her shortly after graduating from high school and had a brief romantic interlude that we never consummated. We became best friends and hung out like wet clothes and though we lost touch for a while, we always remained close and had each other's back. She was one of the sweetest, nicest, kindest, human beings on the planet. She'd give her last to a friend or family member. Angel was a brown-skinned Moor

140

(black) woman who was always smiling or laughing. She was about a size 12 and pleasingly plump in some areas, with short, coarse hair and a heart of gold.

I was always welcomed in her apartment as was she in mine. We watched movies together a couple of times a week. She was always asking what I cooked for dinner and ate at my place every now and then. I was always welcomed to any food she had. I spent the night at her house and slept in the bed with her, and sometimes she slept at my place in the bed with me. It wasn't even about a sexual relationship because we were indeed best friends. Most times, it just felt nice to sleep with a good friend who cared about you. Or, maybe neither of us felt like being alone on certain nights. We never sweated each other about our personal love interests because it didn't matter. Once in a while in the heat of the moment we shared expression which was fun. It was a wonderfully convenient arrangement for us both. I used to school her on men and she gave me the female perspective as it related to my women. When I told Angel that Marshann had a live-in boyfriend and stayed at my place until after 6:40 am, she gave me the skinny, "That woman wanna fuck you, and from what you told me, it's because you didn't cater to her like she's used to... like all them other guys did. Ain't no woman gonna take a risk like that for platonic friendship's sake. And she stayed 'till almost seven this morning? Yeah, you'll have that before the weekend is out." We both cracked up laughing.

That Saturday afternoon I got a call from Marshann, "Did you wanna continue our homework assignment?" I busted out laughing because after all, it really was our homework assignment, but I also remembered what Angel told me. "Yeah Marshann, we can do that." "My boyfriend is working a twelve tonight from seven to seven. So, I can come after seven?" "Ok, that's cool. Hey Marshann, did you think about me today?" Initially she was silent, because she didn't wanna show her vulnerable side. "Uhh... yeah... I did. I had a real good time getting to know you yesterday. Have you been thinkin' about me?" "Hell naw, are you crazy? I'll see yo' high-yellow ass when you get here. And call before you come, just in case one of my women is here. Bye!" She was laughing as I hung up the phone

141

on her. You see, I had to treat Marshann like that because she really thought she was the shit and a pimp-et on top of that. So, I constantly had to break her down. At every opportunity I influenced Marshann to display her soft side... but I never showed her mine. It was all in good fun

Darrell had previously told me Marshann was a freak but that he never fucked her. I found that to be quite interesting because how else would he officially know? So, the combination of her having a live-in boyfriend, being a (potential) freak, plus she was my fellow thespian, coupled with the fact that I wasn't sexually attracted to her and I'd never fuck a woman so soon after meeting her, meant Marshann wasn't getting any tonight or in the future. But as Angel said, my disinterest in Marshann was one of the things that attracted me to her. I noticed she didn't have interest in any of the other guys in the cast (and there were quite a few). So freak or not, Marshann was at least picky.

Marshann buzzed my buzzer around 7:20 pm (which in my estimation, made her look too anxious.) She must've left the house right after her man pulled off for work. When I opened the door she was wearing this tight-ass, short, red silk dress. Her hair was freshly whipped and she had on the adequate amount of make-up that accentuated her beauty. She kinda caught me off guard, "Well are you gonna let me in or make me stand out here? And put your eyes back in your sockets." "Awe whatever! I was just trying to regain my eyesight after you blinded me with that bright-ass dress you got on." "Oh ok I understand, that's your way of saying I look good."

She took her shoes off at the door and her toe nails were also painted red. Red must've been her color because I had to admit, it was very attractive. I asked her why she was so dressed up and she claimed she was going to the club after she left my place, but I didn't buy that as the truth. Her appearance showed way too much effort for a club. I knew she got dolled-up strictly for me. On the contrary, I'd been lounging around in a jogging suit which accentuated the casual vibe I was radiating. I was so focused on Marshann's appearance I didn't see the bag she brought in with her. "I bought you a bottle of wine since we drank yours up last night." Yeah right. I didn't believe that bullshit, she wanted to get me tipsy. I've always had a very, very low tolerance to alcohol. The night before, I only had a half a glass before my speech started slurring and my eyes got tight. But she was obviously a drinker because she drank the rest of the bottle and didn't even get a buzz.

I was curious as to whether her club story was authentic so I questioned her, "What time are you leaving to go to the club?" "I don't know yet, but I don't wanna get there too early 'cause I gotta make my entrance." "Well do you have time to watch a movie?" "Yeah, I do. Wha'chu got...some pornos?" She started laughing as though she was kidding, but that let me know just where her mind was right then. We ran lines for a little while then started the film. About a third of the way through the movie she inquired about the wine. I was in such a cool mode because as attractive as she was looking, I still wasn't interested in her in that way. So as far as I was concerned it was all a part of our homework assignment. Getting acquainted with Marshann was just another role I was playing.

I felt a small buzz coming on after just two small sips of wine and as we were sitting on the couch in my den, I started dozing off. As Marshann caught me dozing, it substantiated my 'you-ain't-all-that' philosophy. "Now I just know you ain't falling asleep on me." I could tell by her tonality she wasn't used to such treatment. "I'm sorry babe I'm still tired from last night. You must've slept in 'cause I didn't get a chance to." "Yeah I slept in." The next thing I knew, Marshann propped her big hairy legs upon my lap (which were very nice. GOD knows I love a hairy woman). Seeing her short dress rise even higher woke me for a few minutes...until I dozed off again. I got so sleepy that she ended up laying my head on her lap. I felt her stroking my hair and rubbing my shoulders as I slept. After a few minutes, Marshann got up and went to the bathroom. Even though I was drugged with sleep, I didn't hear her peeing or the toilet flush. In fact she came out of the bathroom rather quickly. I figured she probably checked her make-up or tested for bad breath. She came back and repositioned herself with my head on her lap and I drifted off to sleep again. I apparently slept till the end of the movie because I heard the soundtrack in my sleep.

There was an extremely sensual aroma in my nostrils that really aroused me. I was semi-awake but my eyes were still closed because I was tired. Suddenly I realized my cheek was no longer resting upon Marshann's silk dress, but upon her bare thigh. As I tilted my head to investigate, I felt hair on the tip of my nose and upper lip. Now I understood why she went to the bathroom earlier... to take her panties off. This freaky 'heafa' had positioned herself to where my head was laying right between her crotch, with her dress raised and panties off, and managed to do it all while I was asleep. Incredible! I looked up to see her fake-ass pretending to be sleep. Yeah she got me! Her aroma was so alluring and her clit was right there. What else was I supposed to do? By then, her scent was all in my being.

I laid on my stomach to reposition myself and see what I was about to get into. Marshann reached down and pulled my sweatshirt off over my head. She started rubbing my shoulders and stroking my back. I tucked my sweatshirt underneath her because I didn't know Marshann and had absolutely no intentions of swallowing any of her juices... not even my own saliva. Also, I didn't want her scent in my couch so my shirt provided the perfect place to aspirate. Marshann had what men refer to as 'wolf pussy', an afro-puff about 3 inches long. I constantly had to push the hair back to gain access to her vagina. I started licking her clit and she opened her legs wider, then she propped her outer leg on my cocktail table... now I had total access (and she was supposed to be sleep, huh?).

I could tell Marshann was gon' cum real quick because her vagina was already soaking wet and her clit was throbbing. Her toes were spread wide enough to put golf balls between them. It took about six minutes for Marshann to climax, which was extremely gratifying for me. She moaned and groaned with such intensity, then broke out into laughter as her orgasm flourished (I just love the way different women uniquely experience their orgasms). That's when she pushed my head back and scooted away from my mouth then we played the chase game. She fell onto the floor trying to get away from me... and further stimulation. I never saw her as the begging type, but she pleaded for me to stop because her sensitivity was just too overwhelming and she needed time to recompose herself.

Marshann's dramatic, fanatical response to my skill and passion made tasting her (and the prospect of doing so) very attractive and fun. Her reactions and responses were also conducive in cultivating a long time fuck-buddy acquaintanceship we shared for many years. I'd always strived to be unique and special, and felt that pleasing women sexually was definitely one way of standing out from average men, whom women termed as 'selfish...and just looking to bust a nut.' But somewhere along the way, I also picked up the propensity not just to please women, but to be a pleaser.

What's the difference between pleasing women and being a pleaser? From the perspective of the men I've associated with, pleasing a woman is mostly egotistical. We wanna be able to say we had you screamin' and hollering all night long, or that you couldn't handle it (whatever pet-name we have for our penis) because it strokes our fragile egos. It's almost like a sport or a challenge to us, you know, something we can talk about at guy's night out. But a pleaser is entirely different. A pleaser's pleasure is directly linked to the pleasure of the person they're pleasing because a pleaser's pleasure IS pleasing. A pleaser doesn't even have to orgasm because they get off mentally as they're partner climaxes physically. A pleaser's primary focus is pleasuring through the expression of pleasing, instead of pleasing through the expression of pleasuring.

Afterward, I got up to rinse out my mouth and grab a blanket. When I returned, Marshann was sitting on the floor fully undressed. She obviously thought we were gonna engage in something more, but I had to put her on notice. I explained how I was attempting to live morally upright (and avoid a guilty conscious. Plus as attractive as she was, she just didn't do it for me, along with the other reasons I mentioned earlier but I didn't tell her all that). Besides she'd had her orgasm which satisfied me, and I was fine without having one because I got my pleasure pleasing her. It seemed like as long as I didn't cum I was fine, but when I did, guilt and conviction would surface. Marshann didn't quite understand my dilemma, but she was more than willing to embrace a concept that allowed me to eat pussy as a way of avoiding guilt... especially when it was her pussy. She was all for it and took full advantage of it.

I spread the blanket on the floor as she described her mundane sexual relationship with her live-in boyfriend, "He's twelve years older than me and we've been together for years, so he's all chilled-out. Shit, we might have sex twice a month the same old way. And he definitely don't eat my pussy." Marshann cursed a lot and talked real raunchy like that, "I've asked him to do it, but he ain't into that so I jus' stopped asking. I ain't gon' lie, I'm a freaky bitch and I'm still young. I gotta do some wild shit every now and then (I guess Darrell was right)."

"Really now, so do you fuck around on your boyfriend often?" "Uh-uhh, it's been a while since I did anything like that. I USED to sometimes before we started livin' together, but that's been two years ago." I warned her, "Alright now, I don't want no shit! Make sure you handle yo' business right, cause I don't want no drama unless it's on stage." "Naw, he ain't like that at all. He's very non-confrontational. If he thought we were fucking around, he definitely wouldn't say shit to you. That's not his style. He's too cool for that. He wouldn't even wanna let me know it bothered him. He might talk to me though... real calm like." "Wow, he's sounds like a real nice guy." "Yeah, he is." "Ok well if he's all that, why yo' high-yellow ass sitting on my floor butt-naked with my mustache smellin' like you? She busted out laughing, "Because of that right there! You'z a silly muthafucka and I like being around yo' crazy ass. I like your energy... your style and your confidence. You'z a sexy muthafucka and that shit turns me on...wait a minute! Muthafucka stop askin' so many god-damn questions about MY boyfriend. Shit, if I ain't talkin' 'bout his ass why are you? I just KNOW you ain't trying to help Ike? 'Cause Ike don't need no muthafuckin help!" The entire cast used to check each other with that line from the movie What's Love Got to Do With It, so we both fell out laughing.

Marshann and I laughed and talked for hours while she was lying on the blanket completely nude. But she was like Chinese food; I got hungry for more soon after I finished eating. However, this time I was ultra-explicit. I pleased her in every possible way my oral affixation could imagine. I satisfied my foot fetish and every other fetish either of us had... I licked, sucked and slurped every inch of her body... several times over. I lifted and twisted her into so many different positions as I tasted her. We really got to know each other. I could tell by the passion behind her kisses and the way she touched me that Marshann was thoroughly open, and utterly and completely satisfied... despite not being penetrated. The blanket was soaking wet in several different spots, totally due to Marshann's excitement. She had so many orgasms she was docile and tamed. And by then, she was as gorgeous to me as everyone else thought she was.

Time flew by so fast and before we knew it, birds were chirping and sunlight was beaming through the shades. She told me her boyfriend was off on Sundays and she probably wouldn't be able to see me. That sounded strange to me. As far as I was concerned, it didn't matter whether we saw each other or not. But Marshann was very smitten by me. I told her I'd see her at rehearsal on Monday and when she left at 6:30 am, I went straight to bed and slept 'till the afternoon. It seemed like the telephone rang a hundred times while I was sleep and when I got up that afternoon and listened to my messages, many of them were from Marshann. It was kinda cute but at the same time, it irritated the shit outta me, BEEEP! "Call me when you get up." BEEEP! "Damn, you still sleep? Call me when you get this message." BEEEP! "I'm sorry I keep calling you so much. But, I can't stop thinkin' 'bout you lickin' my pussy. It's not just that...I been thinkin' about you too...and I miss you." BEEEP! "Bruiser's mad at me. Call me back."

I always nickname every woman's boyfriend, Bruiser! But what's funny about that is they all start calling their boyfriends Bruiser after that. So, when I heard Bruiser was upset, I was curious to discover why, so I called Marshann. "Hey Marshann, what's up?" "Heyyy sleepy-head! You finally woke up, huh? Guess what? Bruiser was home when I got in this morning." "Woe, what did you do?" "I told him that I was out with my sisters. I got four of 'em, and sometimes we do hang out till late morning like that. I tried not to get close to him because I knew your scent was all over me. But when I took a shower, I think he knew something was up." "What time did he get home?" "He said around 5:45 am." "So what did he say?" "He said he was just worried about me because he didn't know where I was and I usually tell him where I'm goin' and what I'm doing. Then, he said he called my sister I mainly hangout with to see if I was with her." "Dayum! So you got cold busted, huh?" "Nuh-uh, my sisters already know what to

147

do in those situations. Trust me, we been doin' this shit a long time. She told him we all went out to the club, and we'd just left her house from playing cards all night long. Then she told him that I might've gone to breakfast before I went home." "Well did he believe you?" "Shit, he didn't have no other choice...what else was he gon' do? I put my dress in the cleaners, so fuck it! You wanna get together and run some lines today?" "Hell naw are you crazy, I'll see yo' scandalous-ass tomorrow at rehearsal." Marshann laughed as I hung up the phone on her.

The following Monday evening at rehearsal I knew the entire cast would be focused upon me and Marshann's every move; however, for different reasons. Of course Craig was looking for a convincing performance. Some of the guys wanted to see just how far I'd taken my getting-to-know homework, while the women looked to see if Marshann penetrated my professional armor and softened me up. I got to rehearsal first and was a bit anxious about how Marshann would respond to me. Also how we'd interact with each other after our weekend activities. I was cool and had no intentions of acting any different than I had before, at least as long as we were around people. But I had a funny feeling that people would be able to tell something by the way Marshann responded to me. When she came through the door, all eyes were on her, then upon the both of us. She was doing an adequate job of remaining low-key and I was so relieved. In fact, for a while, we didn't communicate much at all, which was perfect.

As expected, Craig ran our scenes first and the entire cast offered their undivided attention like never before. Talk about pressure, it felt like the actual performance. From the very beginning it was apparent and extremely obvious there was a tremendous difference in our chemistry... and it was the fact that we HAD chemistry. The room was so quiet you could hear a fly shitting on honey. When we finished our scenes, everybody gave us the strangest standing ovation I'd ever experienced. They all clapped and cheered with a strange expression on their faces, like they hadn't anticipated what they witnessed. Then the room went dead silent after the applause, to the point where it made me uncomfortable. That's when Craig verbalized what everyone else probably wanted to know. "What the hell did y'all do this weekend?" The entire cast busted out laughing, "That

148

was a phenomenal transformation... y'all definitely did something." Marshann and I sat there trying not to blush from the standing ovation or Craig's subtle accusations.

After rehearsal, Craig and Darrell walked up and stared at me in complete silence. I knew what was coming next so I prepared to offer an Oscar-Winning performance, "What's wrong with y'all?" Craig started first, "You fucked her didn't you?" Craig started laughing as Darrell smiled. "What are you talking about? I'm still married going through a divorce, man. Plus I told y'all she wasn't my type." Darrell wasn't buying it, "Man please, they're all your type after midnight, so don't even try it." "Fellas' y'all got it all wrong. We just ran lines and talked a lot. Besides, even if I did... I never kiss and tell." Then I winked at Darrell who was thoroughly convinced. "Yep, he hit it. It's official!"

Here Comes the Judge

The time was drawing near for my divorce to become official, but LB was in denial. She called me two days before the court proceedings and inquired about my authenticity. "Are you really going through with this? I think we should reconsider. We've had some time apart and I think it's time for us to talk about this... for the sake of our son. I don't even have an attorney because I didn't think you were really going through with this." Now, that pissed me off, her using my son as a pawn (but that was just the beginning of her doing that). Besides, I'd heard too many bad examples of people staying together for the sake of their children and it almost never worked out. Our separation provided different results for both of us. For LB, she saw how difficult it was: footing all the bills on her own, running a household on her own, coming home to an empty house. But for me, it was wonderful: having peace of mind, not having to argue all the time, having control over my environment... not to mention being single again. Shit, what was there to talk about? I'd gotten a taste of what I'd considered to be the good life and there was absolutely no way I was turning back. So, I told LB she needed to retain a lawyer because I was definitely going through with it.

At the court just before the proceedings, LB tried to get biblical, "What GOD has brought together let no man put asunder." Yeah, well the only thing about that was GOD didn't bring our marriage together... we did that stupid shit. And, it was my opinion that GOD certainly wasn't responsible to keep together what He didn't put together. The proceeding went so fast it cheapened the marriage ceremony. It only lasted about three minutes once it got started. I felt so free (finally) being officially divorced. It was a load off morally, but financially, it cost me. I was giving LB money weekly for my son's needs and buying most of his accessories at a discount from the store where I worked part time. This was both convenient and cost-effective for me and it satisfied her. Literal 'child support' (via friends of the court) was never a thought for either of us...until that day. LB must've gone to Sharks-R-Us to retain her attorney because she chomped my ass out with the child support. My attorney just sat there like a fuck and kept saying, "That sounds ok. That sounds good." No it didn't, or least not to me it didn't. But she was trying to do as little as possible with my $750 retainer's fee I paid her. I wasn't aware back then that the judge and both of our attorneys were all on the same team, which is a tremendous conflict of interest.

LB was devastated and I had to admit I felt a little sorry for her. But I merely had to reminisce on all the horrible times we had and all the shit she started and trouble she caused me... and figured maybe her devastation was a result of her own personal karma. Up till now, it had only been Mya, Moonbeam and Marshann, but with my divorce being official, I was really ready to let loose...or shall I say get loose!

...And Away We Go!

Several weeks after my divorce, I was still on a natural high. I'd been hanging out something terrible with one of my best friends Big Ced and was dropping him off at home one afternoon. Please allow me to digress for a moment.

...

[Big Ced and I used to hang out like Siamese twins. Big Ced was 6'8" and weighed about 420 pounds (and was murder on small cars (Lol!). He was a few years older than me but had a baby face and the heart of a saint (as long as you didn't anger him). He was like my personal bodyguard whenever we were together, and like Crenshow, Big Ced was closer than a brother. He had the jolliest, most contagious laugh in the world. I saw him at least five days a week because he was the onsite care-taker for the storage facility that housed the company vehicle I drove. Big Ced later revealed to me he didn't particularly like me during the interim period after my boss introduced us. He said I seemed arrogant (which was strange since I'd only shared superficial salutations with him... but many people have said the same thing about me before getting to know me). Initially, I only talked to Big Ced on a need-to basis because I was always very much about my business. However, when you see someone so often and interact even casually, an acquaintanceship can develop, and not long after, a casual relationship. Our evening chats morphed into lengthy conversations as the weeks and months transpired and eventually, we began anticipating our evening diatribes.

Big Ced was an ex: street niggah, thug, hoodlum, and (drug-dealer's) enforcer. He was unleashed upon anyone who owed money, or stole drug money from the dope man (and I heard he could sho' nuff put a hurting on a man too). He claims he's never killed anybody, but I don't know about that because I witnessed his anger and it wasn't pretty.

I introduced Big Ced to religion. He'd never even set foot inside of a church until he went with me. You see, I became his transportation into the city whenever he needed to go (which became quite often once I availed myself) because he lived in a surrounding suburb of Detroit and like Crenshow, also didn't have a driver's license. Since I had church obligations and responsibilities, I often agreed to transport him wherever he needed or wanted to go...however, only after my bible study or choir rehearsal. Big Ced initially scoffed at what he saw and heard in church, but not long after, he started inquiring about GOD and other biblical questions, to which I was only so happy to eloquently explain. Between doing all the

151

shit I've been talking to you about, I became fairly well-versed and re-hearsed in both Aramaic and Koine Greek and taught bible study in the church I attended. I especially focused on the young men, and some years later, I taught preachers, pastors, bishops and elders at a small Christian institute. Many attest that I am a dynamic teacher, possessing the gift, skill and ability to adequately unveil, define and explain difficult, hidden mysteries seemingly impossible to understand. After a while, Big Ced re-quested to go to church with me, and once the brainwashing process be-gan, it became his regular routine. Once the process was complete, he decided to get saved and got baptized. It took four ministers to dunk him in the water then they all started slipping and stumbling as they tried to pull his big ass back up. Trust me that was the funniest shit you ever wanted to see in life. I damn near urinated on myself AND 'bout had a seizure trying to hide my laughter in the serious atmosphere of the sacred ceremony

Big Ced was a classic functional illiterate. I mean, he could count the shit outta some money, but he couldn't really read or write. You never would've known it because he was very functional and extremely person-able. He had me and virtually everybody around him fooled, but his brother and immediate family, who ironically took terrible advantage of him. I don't know if he was functionally illiterate because he lacked the mental capacity or because of a closed head injury he sustained as a re-sult of being hit by a car years prior. He finally disclosed his handicap to me when he sought to leave his job and I took him to fill out job applica-tions. He tried his best to hide it from me. One day, he waited until we were eating to ask me the strangest question. "Hey doc, can you fill out this application for me?" "What? Why would I fill out your application? Why can't you do it?" "I'm eating." Then he started laughing. "Well, I'm eating too... uhh... I guess you could always wait till you finish eating (duh!)." Afterward, he started on the application. It was one of those real simple ones too, and 15 minutes later, he'd only written his name and it looked like a right-handed child wrote it with their left hand. I knew some-thing was wrong at that point. "Man, ain't no use in me tryna play it off. Besides, you're my man anyway so I can tell you. I can't really read or write too well." I felt so sorry for Big Ced and I also felt a lot of anger toward his brother and family for taking such advantage of his handicap. From that day forward, I vowed not to let anyone take advantage of Big Ced... if I could help it. I helped him in any and every possible way I could and became his personal chauffer.

As the onsite caretaker and groundskeeper of a huge storage facility, Big Ced unofficially inherited all unclaimed items either abandoned or forfeited through unpaid storage fees, and I benefited greatly from the many valuables because he always offered me first dibs on everything he didn't want for himself. Clothing was the majority of what was left behind, from baby clothes on up, and I often sorted through them to see what was available for me. There were never any clothes left that he could fit because he was so damn big. By the end of the year, Big Ced had amassed so many unclaimed clothes he housed them in a large storage unit. He thought of the grand idea of dressing up like santa clause and delivering the clothing as gifts to homeless shelters and domestic abuse shelters. He also purchased a couple hundred dollars worth of toys and trinkets from the dollar store as additional gifts to go along with all the clothes. Man, Big Ced had such a mighty big heart! Then, I thought of the idea of making a party out of sorting the clothes and wrapping all the gifts.

We had it at my place. I called up a bunch of fine ass honeys (as Big Ced referred to women) and a few other guys to help out. We had pizza and movies and everyone was really into the holiday spirit of giving. Now that's what the season is really about... giving to the less fortunate. We had so much damn fun! It took us all night to finish and the last few hours we all just fell asleep on each other in my living room.

We got up very early the next morning and headed out. Big Ced had also rented a moving truck from the storage facility (that I had to drive, of course). There was so much stuff that we damn near filled up the entire truck. Now, big Ced found the largest santa clause outfit he could find, but it was still way too small for his big jolly ass. As we entered each of the shelters and centers around Detroit, there were so many children there that it was mind boggling. It was shocking to see so many men there too. The children stared at Big Ced in disbelief, not only because they weren't expecting santa to show up at a shelter, but because he was so damn big and tall! All the adults were entertained by santa's extra small outfit and laughed their asses off. Big Ced enjoyed every second of it because he always made himself the center of attention, even to the point of being a spectacle, despite the fact he didn't really have to do much to be the center of attention.]

...

We'd been hangin' out and I was dropping him off at home. Just before we arrived at his house, we saw this attractive, dark brown sista driving a gray convertible Fiero with the top down. She had on sunglasses and her head scarf blew in the wind as she drove... she looked so Hollywood. I pulled beside her to catch her eye, and we both started vying for her attention, which she apparently found amusing. I signaled for her to pull over as we bet on who'd get her first. When I parked, Big Ced and I bolted from the car like two little children running to McDonalds. I ran to the driver's side and Big Ced eventually got to the passenger's side (he had trouble getting out the car). She turned her head from side to side like she was at a tennis match as we each spit our game, but Big Ced got first dibs. "Wow! Now you are a big man. What's your name?" "My name is Cedward, but they call me Big Ced." "Yeah, and I can see why." Then she turned to me, "And you're mighty handsome... and dapper. So what's your claim to fame?" Big Ced and I hemmed her up for about ten minutes with our Mack attacks, and we're tied for the win until I told her I was starring in a play. She instantly turned her full attention towards me and Big Ced lost our bet.

I gloated in victory as we arrived at Big Ced's house. He was a bit of a sore loser, "That's ok though...I hope it don't work out for ya', and I hope she's half crazy too." Then we shared a laugh, "But, lem'me know how everything goes." Rhoda and I made tentative plans to see each other later that evening, which I also rubbed in Big Ced's face. But, I was a little surprised when she called me at home shortly after she'd arrived home (this was still before the cell phone age). I was really feelin' my own sexy and was sho' nuff humming in her ear. I gave her my address and I can't recall who asked whom to come over, but Rhoda showed up at my place less than an hour later. I was excited she accelerated our meeting time, because other than regularly tasting Marshann, I hadn't really copulated since Moonbeam, and I was more than ready to express myself.

Also, new pussy, or the prospect thereof, is just exciting in and of itself. I figured it would take a couple of weeks at the most. Nevertheless, Rhoda entered my apartment like she was strolling through a museum. She sat on the couch a half seat cushion away from me with one leg underneath her. We started a basic dialogue and soon rested our arms on the back of the couch, a sure sign of comfort. I subtly checked her out from head to toe and as we talked I discovered she wasn't quite as attractive as she initially appeared. Rhoda was very wonderfully dark with short coarse permed hair. Her teeth were straight and white, but white mostly due to the contrast ratio against her dark skin. Her eyes were very bright, but perhaps brighter for the same reason. Rhoda had a peculiar shape. She was about a size 14 with broad sloping shoulders, long arms and big legs. I couldn't see that earlier as she sat in her car, but even still, she was real cute and very articulate.

We got into a real deep and interesting conversation that took a real creepy turn... and all I could think about was Big Ced's last statement. Rhoda said she'd spent some time in the military, but I noticed she didn't account for a couple of years in her recent past. I thought that was kinda strange so I dug deeper. I mean, what did I have to lose? The most she could've said was, "That's none of yo' business!" But, she reluctantly told me she also spent some time in prison. The penitentiary!? All I could hear was Big Ced's jolly laugh in my head. I almost dreaded to ask her why she was incarcerated. And yes, my blood began to run cold in my veins. "Well, it wasn't a regular prison. It was an insanitarium." "Uhh... what is that?" I heard the word insane in there, but I didn't quite know what it was. "It's a mental hospital and penitentiary combined." My blood ran even colder in my veins and my heart started beating faster. Oh yeah, and Big Ced's laugh got louder too. "So... uhh... why did you go to prison?" She sighed, "Because I tried to kill my husband." (Oh my God!)

My blood ran ice cold in my veins and my heart was beating outta my chest. I thought to myself, what the fuck have I gotten myself into now? You know how your mind starts playing tricks on you? I didn't know if she was gonna whip out a chain-saw and start hacking' me up or what. So I kept a close watch on her hands. At that moment I decided, if she goes for her purse, I was gon' fuck her up! But, I tried my best to play it off, "Oh, ok uhh well... I'm sure he deserved it."

I didn't want her to know I was alarmed so I remained calm. I actually felt more afraid for her than of her because I didn't want her to go in her purse for some lip gloss and end up beat to death in my apartment. But she explained, "My husband was very abusive to me... and... I just couldn't take it anymore." "Wow! What did he do?" Yeah, I know I was prying, and something told me I was about to open a big can of worms. But shit, I'd already come this far. Besides, I was genuinely curious. "Well, he used to make me have sex with his friends... other police officers. Sometimes he watched, and other times he participated. A few times, he watched me with two or three of his friends." I was in a total state of shock, "How long did that go on?" "For about three years. I threatened to tell, but he said nobody would believe me because he was a police chief."

Then, her eyes started watering, and I was like... oh shit! I didn't know whether she was 'bout to snap or what. "He told me if I told, he'd take our son away from me. I knew he could do it because of his position and his connections. So I let it continue. Then one day, I just couldn't take it anymore and I stabbed him eight times. So... he had me put away and I haven't seen my little boy since then." "Wow... well how long has that been?" "Three years." Then she just started boo-hooing. I couldn't believe it! I handed her some tissue and followed my natural instinct to hug and console her. Shit, I was damn near crying myself. I felt her tears on my cheek as they ran down her face. Her wound hadn't healed yet... not even after three years.

I hugged her for what seemed like an eternity and attempted to pull away from her firm embrace a few times, but I didn't want to seem insensitive by releasing our embrace before she was ready to, so I continued. But when we finally parted, she started kissing my cheek, softly and slowly... while she was still crying. It completely threw me off guard and I didn't know what to do. I thought, Oh shit, now she's completely lost it. Suddenly, the thought crossed my mind that I'd never take advantage of a woman in this situation. And, I reassured myself by thinking, I'd never fucked a woman on the same day I met her. Then I said to myself, I'd never fuck a woman I just met without protection. I knew this whole situation was totally under my control. If I decided to be the gentleman I was, she'd cease her advances. But, if I sought to be scurvy and take advantage of the situation, she'd allow me to. Now, something told me not to look in her eyes. As soon as I did, she kissed me right in the mouth. I could've stopped her at that point, and probably should've. But I didn't, and after she kissed me on the mouth a few times, I responded by parting my lips, which seemed to open a flood gate of emotions for her. Even with her nose running, we started kissing like it was our last day on earth. After I went from her lips, to her cheek, to her neck...it was a wrap!

Emotions ran high and we got caught up in the moment. All the while I was thinking what a bastard I was for allowing this to happen, how sleazy I was to allow this to happen just after meeting her, and how nasty and stupid I was for even contemplating the inevitable without condoms. But what could I do? She started unbuttoning my shirt and it was all in the flow. Everything was happening so smoothly and deliberately, it felt natural. Before I knew it, we were both stark naked and I laid her on my living room floor and asked GOD to protect me, since I didn't have any condoms. Now ain't that some dumb shit, askin' GOD to bless my mess? But that's how we do! Now don't be judgmental towards me, because you've done the same thing, something similar... or far worse. For example, just think about when you buy a big greasy hamburger with fries knowing its bad for your cholesterol, fattening and full of harmful toxins. Yet, you pray and ask 'da Lawd' above to bless that poisonous garbage you call food, "for the nourishment of your body... Amen!"

As soon as I inserted, it appeared to electrify her. All that shit I previously thought about... what I never did, or thought I'd never do went right out the window. My dick was so hard, my erection was pulling the skin on my ass and her response to me was so very over-zealous. I mean, it was really over the top. She had me wondering if she'd just been released from prison that day. Her response also boosted my ego, to the point where I started talking shit in her ear. But then I thought, she might have a flashback from her abusive past and roll me over and drive a stake through my heart or something. But to my surprise, her expression was very open and uninhibited. After her third orgasm, I started making her keep count of them and keep me posted as they formed and occurred; that was all some ego shit, but it was magnificent! She was crying (real) tears of ecstasy. My encounter(s) with Rhoda towed the line between passion and lust and to this day, I'm still not clear which was most prevalent. Probably passion because lust always made me feel more convicted. And I didn't really feel guilty during or after our encounter(s). All I know is she was wonderful for my ego. Up to that time, I'd never influenced a woman to have more than three orgasms. So that evening was one of great triumph for me because she counted a total of seven before I came once. You couldn't tell me shit that day!

Big Ced laughed his ass off for a half hour as I told him what happened. He was in tears and at times begged me to stop so he could compose himself before I continued. "Maaaan! I'm soooo glad you got her and not me 'cause I don't need no more crazy women in my life." After that, Big Ced started calling me the shark because I took advantage of a damsel in distress. For some reason I had the craziest notion that I was the one hunted in that scenario because Rhoda was certainly not the victim nor was she in distress. If you ask me, it seemed like she'd planned our encounter from the very beginning. But I kinda felt sorry for her and was genuinely concerned. Rhoda started coming over about twice a week for her 'therapy' and mentally disturbed or not, she was hi-strung, hi-energy and passionate in a semi-freaky way. Rhoda and Marshann served two completely different purposes in my (sex) life. I never fucked Marshann because despite the fact she was gorgeous to most men, I wasn't attracted to her in that way. But she was definitely my taster's choice and she visited weekly so I could taste her. Rhoda had become my main Jane, but I was only blending honey with her. I never tasted her because even though she was clean, she had a strong vaginal aroma that wasn't conducive for me tasting her. I didn't see my relationship with Rhoda going very far, but the lovin' was great so I decided to let things play out. But surprisingly, we kept it going for about a year and during that time she introduced me to the new skool.

New Skool

Rhoda really did have some issues and at times, I thought she was crazy than a muthafucka. Sometimes as we were talking in my living room, she'd just get up and leave... in mid-sentence. I'd be thinking she was in the bathroom and after about five minutes, I'd go looking for her and she'd be sitting in my den. I let it pass the first few times she did it. Then I let her know how it irritated the fuck outta me. "Hey, why do you keep walking out the room without warning? That shit is rude, Rhoda!" She started crying and talking about her son (I never got the correlation, but...). So from that point on, I just let her get away with it. Anyhow, Rhoda and I talked a lot and became very well-acquainted. We got along wonderfully. She often talked about her girlfriend who lived near me and how she wanted us to meet so we could all hang out together. I told her it was alright with me. Rhoda said sometimes she spent the night over her girlfriend's place whenever they hung out real late and said she often thought about dropping by my place since her girlfriend lived so close. But I told her I didn't play that dropping by shit. She used to tell me how she was suspicious of her girlfriend being bi-sexual or something. Personally speaking, I don't believe there's any such term as bi-sexual. Any human being that's (consistently i.e. more than once) intimately involved with his or her same gender is gay... flat-out bottom-line, point blank and period! It doesn't matter whether he or she is also involved with his or her opposite gender because that's the universal natural order and cosmic balance. I'm not passing judgment on homosexuality I'm just stating my personal opinion which was derived from the bible, religion and the dominate folkways, morays, and traditions of my youth. I mean, who am I to be so judgmental, right?

After Rhoda unveiled her suspicion about her girlfriend, it took a minute for me to assimilate what she'd told me in previous conversations. "Hold on, hold on... wait a minute! You mean to tell me you spend the night at her place and suspect she's gay? Does she know you suspect it?"

"No, I don't think so, at least I've never told her of my suspicion." "Well, why do you think she's gay?" "Because of some of the things she says and does." "Like what?" "I mean, she's real touchy-feely with me. She's always complimenting my appearance and I ain't ever known her to have a steady boyfriend even though I know she fucks guys." "Well, that doesn't really mean anything. Has she ever tried anything with you?" "Nah, not really. She's never done that." As we spent time over the days and weeks, Rhoda said her girlfriend was anxious to meet me since she'd told her so much about me. I talked to her on the phone a few times when Rhoda was over; she sounded real cool.

One evening, Rhoda disclosed some more interesting information as we were talking about apartment sizes and rent prices in my neighborhood. She told me how much her girlfriend paid for her one bedroom apartment. It took me a few seconds, but I questioned her again, "Hold up! You spend the night at your friend's and she only has a one bedroom apartment? Where do you sleep?" "We sleep in her bed, but at opposite ends." "Rhoda, you're gonna end up leading her on. And, she's never tried anything on you? If she is gay, she's eventually gonna try you, especially if you remain naïve about this." A few days later, Rhoda called me and told me her girlfriend finally tried something. "We'd been drinkin' and were both kinda tore-up, so it might've just been the alcohol." "What did she do?" "She walked in on me while I was using her bathroom, but she apologized." "That's all?" "Then, she tried to kiss me." "For real? On the lips?" "Kinda. Right at the corner of my mouth, but I stopped before she got a second chance." "Then you left?" "No, I stayed because I couldn't drive. I mean, we were really blitzed." "So where did you sleep?" "I still slept in her bed because she didn't try anything else. But, I don't think I'm gonna spend the night over there anymore." "Well' no shit Sherlock... you think? I told you she was gonna try something, didn't I? "Yeah, I guess you were right."

The more Rhoda and I expressed our passions, the more we wanted to. But, I could never get over her over-zealous response to my form of expression. I mean, I knew I was that guy when it came to blending honey, but damn! On one occasion, I just watched the tears stream from Rhoda's eyes as she was straddled upon me gyrated back and forth. She really appeared to be in utter ecstasy. I was inclined to ask her afterward, "Rhoda, why do you respond to me like that?" "Because you have a unique energy (then she chuckled). Honey, you underestimate yourself... you got that magic wand." "Did you respond to the last guy like that?" "What last guy?" "I don't know, your man, your boyfriend... whoever you were with before me." She looked at me with pity, "Look... you remember when I said my girlfriend was bi-sexual and she tried something on me? Well, it's really the other way around. I'm bi-sexual and I've been trying her." Oh my God, I was in total shock because that was the absolute first time I'd ever encountered anything like that, at least to my conscious knowledge.

Back in 1992, I was real ignorant to the whole gay thang. I've always been straight old-skool and always associated with like kind. So, I just sat there with my mouth hanging open in total silence... and she continued. "When I went to prison, I kinda picked it up there. It was safe for me. I mean, I didn't trust men anymore because of what my ex-husband had done to me... and his friends... and those damn perverted-assed prison guards. So, I just continued after I got out. Then, I went to the military. It was there too! So you're the first man I've been with since my husband. I mean, I have a toy at home, but it damn sure ain't you. It doesn't have your energy and charming personality, you know?" Then she laughed. "Wow...ok. So, why am I the golden child, huh? Why am I the first man you got with?" "Because you have a beautiful spirit. You're a good person, you have a good heart... and I trust you." "But, you didn't know that the day we met." "Yeah, I did. I knew it when you first talked to me at my car, and I also knew we were gonna get together."

Rhoda really made me feel very special...but I went off on her afterward. "That was unfair for you to keep that from me. You should've given me the choice of whether I wanted to deal with you or not." Back then everybody, including me, was anxious about the risk of a.i.d.s., especially as it related to interactions with gay women. "I'm sorry sugar. You wanna break things off?" "It's too late now! Shit, we've already been involved." I finally figured out that's probably the reason why Rhoda was so anxious for me to meet her girlfriend, so we could all get together. I told Rhoda I was old-skool, "I'm straight, and I only mess with one woman at a time. I ain't never done a threesome and prior to you, I'd never even thought about it." "You see, that's why I like you. You're a good, wholesome man. It's probably best we didn't all get together because I probably would've ended up getting jealous. I'm really enjoying being with a man again. You've brought me back into proper balance with myself. I love you for that."

I started going through more than a few women who all seemed to remain in my life to offer me a life lesson or offer some clarity in one way or another. It wasn't like I really had 'em cummin' and goin' like a lot of my other Moor (black) brothas. I simply love(d) the company of women. I had a few male friends, but very many female friends. I felt secure, complete and balanced around them. I loved their energy... their femininity. It seemed that every woman who entered my life was hand-picked. Most times, women engaged me. I can't recall very many times when I initiated the chase. Some of that was because I'm real laid back in my approach because I despise rejection, probably more than the average man. Another part of it is the early philosophy I picked up regarding the equal value of gender genitals. I was never going to be (or appear to be) pressed for some pussy. Why, when I possessed something women were pressed for?

I was living a dual life of religiosity and carnality. Yeah, I was at church two to three days a week and all day on Sundays. Sure, I was reading and studying the bible daily while teaching its doctrines. Yes, I was becoming familiar with religious dogma and how it affected the human spirit and mind. But on the weekend and sometime during the week, I had to be a man... a human being. I had such internal turmoil regarding these issues. So, in my own demented thinking, in exchange for my sins, I always introduced the women I was involved with to the church, the bible, religion or GOD... or a combination of the four, because they're all very unique and distinct. But that seemed to set up other issues. Some women started questioning the authenticity of my faith and commitment (to the four) as I continued sinning with them. Some women picked up guilt and began feeling their own conviction. And, some were just very empathetic as they witnessed my personal struggle with the entire issue. Little did I know, I was really confusing the shit out of some women who didn't quite understand my personal internal issues and unfortunately, there is corresponding Karma that comes along with that.

Karma is like the urge to urinate. Have you ever had to pee so badly that you started doing the pee dance? (I truly believe that's how a lot of new dances are created). While you're beating on the bathroom door begging for whomever to come out, the pee dance is that uncontrollable rhythmic movement you do before the door opens. And as you well know, you can only hold back just so long before you relinquish control. Karma's quite the same way. You can't stop it and when you've built up enough either way, negative or positive... it explodes on the scene, sorta like a jackpot payout, and there's absolutely nothing you or anyone else can do about it. You can't pray it off, you can't cry it away, you can't lie yourself out of it or bargain with it. However, you can pay it off by building positive Karma. However, sometimes it takes as long to build up positive Karma as it did to build up and pay out the negative.

Cher-e-e-e-e-e-ery Ba-ya-be!

After a brief hiatus, we resumed the play production and auditioned a few new prospects. Most of the models that were once a part of the initial production were gone and the cast was scaled down to a much smaller size. Craig was moving the production to a larger venue and sought to cut costs wherever he could. I always loved the introduction and auditioning of new talent, it's sorta like fresh meat. You get to observe the new competition and the different energies and nuances they bring to the production. And to me, everybody was competition because it was my stage... my applause... my laughter... my standing ovations... and my autographs they were all competing for. One of the women being auditioned brought her sister along, who was rather attractive. But for whatever reason, I hadn't paid her much attention because I was so involved with the audition process. At the end of the long, grueling audition process (and

163

rehearsal), Craig started acting silly (as he often would) and told the woman's sister I was interested in her and wanted her phone number. You know how guys try to put each other on the spot to purposely embarrass each other? Initially, she didn't believe Craig or take the bite, but it backfired on him after his third attempt... and she let him have it. "Uhh, I believe this man can speak for himself. If he wants my phone number, I'm sure he knows how to ask me for it." Then she looked at me, "I don't really take Craig seriously because I can see he plays a lot... so, do you really want my phone number?" Now she put me on the spot. The room fell completely silent and it seemed like everybody held their breath in anticipation of my answer. I had no intentions of talking to her or asking for her number, but the pressure got the best of me (and as I looked her over, she was... sufficient). So, I accepted, "Uhh yes, I'd like to have your number."

I took a couple of days to call Cherry and our initial conversation was pretty mundane. Personally, I didn't think she was gonna make it very far. It seemed like I was trying too hard to maintain interest in our conversation. But every time I looked at the clock, another hour had passed. So obviously, something was maintaining my attention. The next thing I knew it was 3 o' clock in the morning. We started calling each other on a semi-regular basis (at night) and we'd talk until the early morning. I decided to really take my time to slowly cultivate an acquaintanceship and finally invited her over after several weeks. I quickly discovered she was actually more than... sufficient.

Cherry was 5'5", size twelve, very voluptuously shaped and bow-legged from the hips down (there's nothing sexier than a bowlegged woman). She was chocolate brown and very pretty with sleepy, bedroom eyes and a sexy disposition. She had dimples and a beautiful smile. She wore her hair in a fashionably short style. Cherry had the look of a high-maintenance woman. But as I got to know her, I discovered she was the sole provider of her high-maintenance costs. She had a very good job with a local news paper and had purchased a quaint little house; of which she was very proud. She was always doing little things to and around her house to improve it. She also had a raggedy little car, a Ford Escort. Cherry had two pretty little girls, ten and seven years old, one by her ex-husband and the other by her ex-boyfriend. About a year and a half prior to us meeting, her ex-boyfriend had beat her up real bad and thrown her and her two daughters out on the street. She showed me some pictures of her abuse. It was ugly! Seeing those photographs made me real angry and an instant enemy of her ex-boyfriend. I reasoned with her, "How can a muthafucka kick his own daughter out? I mean, even if I had problems with you, I wouldn't kick my own daughter out with you. That's some real stupid shit!" But a year or so after their break-up, Cherry was doing fine, living the American Dream... except for that raggedy ass car (Lol!).

I invited Cherry over one Friday evening and we sat on my living room floor talking half the night, like we usually did over the phone... when things suddenly turned intimate. Cherry was 27 (three years older than me) and her apparent maturity and settled disposition was extremely attractive to me. I simply love a woman who knows exactly what she wants and doesn't waver in her thinking... a woman who's very decisive and settled in herself. I didn't have any real intensions on romancing her that night, but it just sorta naturally happened. Cherry was the most mature woman I'd dealt with up until that time. Mya, Moonbeam and Marshann had never been married, nor did either of them have children. And though Rhoda was divorced with a son, he was in his father's custody. None of them had their own house with children they cared for, which brings me to one of the most attractive things about Cherry. She was a real, good mother to her daughters. She was an excellent provider and always exhibited that special motherly love. But when either of her daughters stepped out of line (and it didn't take much), she got in their ass and disciplined them. I loved her for that. So many single moms nowadays try to befriend their children (especially their daughters) instead of being their parents.

Cherry was the first woman I encountered where I didn't immediately feel like I had the upper hand sexually. Her disposition was calm, yet confident and I got the feeling she was sizing me up as she seduced me. She didn't seem surprised, overwhelmed or taken off-guard by my sexual prowess like my previous victims... I mean, acquaintances (Lol!). She sorta made me feel like the subordinate... and I enjoyed the way she seduced me; it was so sexy. She stared straight into my eyes the whole time. I loved the way she softly grazed the back of my head with her long finger-nails as she kissed me. She kept chuckling, which made me feel a little insecure. What the fuck was she chuckling about? It might've just been a psychological move because I was certainly psyched out. She also kept talking to me in her smooth, controlled, breathy, sensual tone... which drove me crazy. "You alright?" she'd chuckle. "Uhh-huh, I'm fine." Then, she handled my ears. Shit! It was uncanny how she knew all of my spots. Cherry looked through me like she had foreknowledge of how to fulfill my every desire and chuckled because she was amused by her accuracy. This was brand new territory for me because I was always the one in control. But it felt more erotic relinquishing it to a sophisticated lover.

We never made it to the bedroom though. I grabbed the pillows and blankets from my bed (and some towels). She took off her blouse and bra and was well-endowed. I figured fondling and sucking her titties would put me back in control of the situation. And though she responded wonder-fully to my passionate expression, I became a little anxious when it was her turn to express. Her eyes lit up when I took my shirt off. I was in the best physical shape of my life... and I knew it. She whispered in that sexy tone of hers, "Sit down on the couch." She kneeled between my opened legs and gripped my chest... almost in disbelief. "Damn, you have a nice body!" She grabbed and fondled my entire torso, like she was orchestrat-ing a symphony.

Afterward she honed in on my nipples. That's my main G spot! (I must have a sign on my forehead telling women where my "spot" is). She knew it too, "Mmm-hmm, that's it right there... come here." I sat up on the edge of the couch, then she chuckled before nibbling... licking... and suck-ing the brown off my nipples. Cherry took her sweet time with everything she did and I really appreciated that because it enabled me to mentally replay all of her actions in my mind right after she did them, which is over-whelmingly engaging. I just leaned my head back against the couch and moaned. I was trying not to lose further control, but she made that more difficult by talking shit. "That's ok baby, let it all out." And the more she talked shit, the greater became my urge to moan. It felt so good. I started backing away from her passion, which was another first for me.

"Wait a minute. Did I tell you to back away from me, huh?" At that very moment, she'd officially placed me in my most vulnerable position of subordinate... and she was my superior. There have only been a few women throughout my lifetime who've been able to place me in that position. They have to have a delicate balance of having the right kind of personality along with a sensual attitude... and we have to have the right chemistry. Well, Cherry had it all and she was the first to do it. "Now, where do you think you goin'? Take them pants off!" I damn near came when she said that. I could feel this intense sensation deep in my anal canal that was driving me crazy! When I stood up to undo my pants, Cherry sat down on the floor to one side on her hip supported by her hand. That's when I realized her pants were already off. Now, how the fuck she did that while seducing me was impressive and amazing. Cherry was smooth. Once I dropped my pants Cherry smiled at my erection, perhaps because it was throbbing at the head. Then she looked up at me with a seductive smile, almost satisfied that she'd caused it to throb. She slowly came to her knees without taking her focus off my erection. Her smile dissipated and was replaced by a virtual hypnotic expression. The anticipation was unbearable.

First, she came so close to my penis (without touching it) that I could feel her exhales. Then when the throbbing became one long throb, she gently grabbed it with one hand and griped my ass cheek with her other hand for balance. She slowly... sweetly... sensually... and seductively orally expressed herself like she'd found her long, lost lover while I whimpered and moaned like a lost little child. I gradually descended upon the edge of the couch then slowly slid down off the couch onto the floor... and Cherry never skipped a beat. I don't know how she did it but she never stopped her oral expression.

I ended up lying on my back on the floor with my legs propped on the couch while she continued her onslaught. She positioned her vagina in my face, but I didn't go for the 69 set up. I'd already planned to taste her at some point, however, on my own terms and in my own time. I was trying my best not to cum. It would've been so embarrassing. So shortly before I was about to release, I beckoned for her to switch places, "Lay down, honey." Fuck that! I wasn't about to go out like a punk, so I had to even up the score. I offered Cherry my most passionate and sensual oral expression available. I took my time and became 'the moment'.

...

For those who don't understand 'the moment', it's when your entire body... your very person simply ceases to exist. You're no longer in your body, but actually become the body part you're expressing your passion through. Fellas, close your eyes and allow yourself to come with me. Now just embrace the darkness of the cosmos and with intensely focused energy and concentration, transfer all that you are into your lips and tongue so that you literally become... your lips and tongue. And imagine her vagina as the only matter in existence. Or, with that same focused energy and concentration, transfer everything you are into your penis... and all that you penetrate and peruse is the only matter in existence. I realize this might seem like a strange occurrence that's difficult to understand if you've never experienced it. Some phenomena can be kinda difficult to articulate and describe, but some of y'all really overstand what I'm talking about. And it's only when you open your eyes and return to your original estate that you realize you're even in the world again and how much damage you've caused from the focused energy of passion you've exerted.

When I opened my eyes, it was the first time I'd focused on her moans, groans and cries (yeah, I was that far gone). She came so heavily not only were my mustache and mouth drenched, but her juices shot up through my nostrils back into my throat and I expectorated her excess honey. She had me choking like I'd just took a hit on some organic cannabis. Now the score was at least tied. After she rode out the last wave of her orgasm, she propped a pillow behind her head and motioned for me to kiss her. She kissed and licked all her juices off my face. Now, that's the way you're supposed to express yourself! Now you can overstand why good hygiene has always been so important to me. While I was on top, she inserted me into her and it was amazing that she was so wet but still offered so much resistance. I was surprised to discover her vagina was so snug. And though that was good to me, it wasn't necessarily good for me, if I had any intention of lasting longer than five minutes. Man, this was a fantasy!

Her sounds of passion accelerated my feeling to release, but I couldn't disclose that to her because I knew what would happen. "Shhh, baby please be quiet your voice is soooo sexy." Her facial expression changed when I said it... and I knew I was in trouble. Once she discovered I was overwhelmed (yeah, initially her lovin' was almost unbearable) and all she had to do to break me down was talk shit in my ear, it was only a matter of time. She peered deep into my eyes and smiled as she spoke softly and slowly, "You alright, baby... huh?" My moans became more intense. "That's ok, express yourself. Don't hold it back baby... let it all go. I know you ain't had good loving like this before... you're just a baby." "Cherry, please shut the hell up!" She chuckled, "Uh-uhh, why you want me to stop talkin'? Is it good to you... huh? Is this lovin' too much for you?"

Every time I tried to close my eyes or turn my head she'd turn my head back toward her and tell me to open my eyes. I knew full-well what she was doin'. She was placing her image deep down into my psyche, so even if I closed my eyes or turned away, I'd still see her. To keep from releasing, I attempted to pull out, but she clinched her PC muscles and put it on me. God-damn her voice was sexy! Then she laid down the law. "Now let me tell you how this gon' go." Whenever she spoke, she released her PC muscles, but when she demanded an answer, she clinched them before my response (I prayed the night would never end). "From now on... until we decide differently... this is my dick. OK?" She smooth stroked me as she clutched and released her PCs. Shit! I was helpless, "Yesss." "Uh-uhh, I can't hear you... and say my name niggah?" She punked me, but I loved it. "Yessss Cherry yesss!"

She was ahead on the score card so I had to save face. I went deeper and her eyes rolled back in her head. This was my opportunity. I resurfaced, "Uhh-uh, bitch... open your eyes and look at me." I didn't really mean to say that, but it came out in the moment and luckily for me, she responded favorably to it. "Whose bitch are you?" Cherry smiled then chuckled as she initially refused to answer that question on our first encounter... and so soon. So, I propped her legs up on my shoulders and went as deep as I could. She screamed and moaned as I slowly made wide circles with my hips... for about 45 *good* minutes. Once I let her down, I reiterated the question and she relented, "Shit! Baby, I'm your bitch for as long as you want me to be."

I guess I showed her, but I knew it wasn't quite over. She told me to lie down on my back. Then she straddled me. I knew even though I'd tied the score and won the battle, she was about to win the war. She eased down upon me as a confident expression came over her face. She started slowly moving back and forth upon me. It was so smooth like she was hoola-hooping in slow motion; it brought tears to my eyes. She leaned forward and supported her hands upon my chest, then flashed that beautiful smile with those dimples and slowly shook her head from side to side. "I really like you... and we're gonna have a wonderful friendship. You know that don't you?" I'd already thought the same thing and it was just good to know we shared the same sentiments. "But in response to your question"...she clutched her PCs and placed a vice-lock grip upon my dick. Now that was sexy! I closed my eyes and reared my head back. My mouth flew open, but not a sound came out. It was just as well because she did all the talking anyway.

She spoke to me in the rhythm of her hip strokes, like a parent spanks their child to the rhythm of their scolding. "Whenever you need some lovin'...you come to me, you hear me? Because this dick belongs to me and me only! Ain't that right? And it's just me and you... you hear me?" Then she closed her eyes, gnawed her bottom lip and reared her head back as she rode my erection in ecstasy. I was awe-stricken and in complete silence from overwhelming stimulation and my silent consent was her confirmation. By then Cherry had become just a little cocky, "Mmm-hm. That's just what I thought...I do good work." Then she smiled.

In past times, I was always the one in control, calling shots and deciding the levels and intensity of passion and erotica. But for the first time in my young life, I had a woman who not only could hold her own, but took me where I'd never gone before in ecstasitic heights. It felt divine as I basked uninhibitedly in it. As she finished talking, a deep groan welled up in the pit of my stomach and as I released it, my toes curled and that intense stimulation in my anal canal exploded. "Get-up baby, I'm 'bout to cum!" Cherry leaped off me with calm anticipation as we watched it shoot a foot into the air (which had never happened to me before). She smiled in approval and I grabbed and hugged her like she'd just saved my life. She sat with her back up against my couch and held me with my face against her bosom like a mother cuddles her lil' baby. We eventually drifted off to sleep in silence and woke up on my living room floor. As our eyes opened to each other's face the next morning, we smiled simultaneously.

Cherry was a fun-loving, wonderful woman who was very easy to be around. We were a perfect match. She smiled at the simplest things and cried at tender moments. She appreciated the small things, which made her easily excitable and she celebrated her femininity with great sex appeal. We started going together without verbal confirmation. I guess you could say it officially started the first night we made love. The unique part about our relationship was that it was all encompassing. She played several different roles for me: Cherry demonstrated a motherly love and concern toward me while maintaining the camaraderie of a friend. We also maintained a sibling type kinship that inspired us to watch each other's back, no matter what. All this, while being a phenomenal and extraordinary lover with a touch of nasty girl.

Cherry had a real good heart and was kind, considerate and patient. But most of all, she LOVED my last-week's dirty drawers. Yeah that was my girl, and I loved her too. She could cook her ass off. After we started goin' together, she began grocery shopping with me in mind. I thought that was the sweetest thing. I used to tell her not to grocery shop for me and she'd get so upset, "Why not? You need to eat and I'm cooking every day. It only makes sense that I cook for you too, especially with you being so busy. You need to eat a home cooked meal." I finally stopped fighting her about it. Another very interesting thing about us was we made love damn near every day and it never, ever got stale, routine or lost any of its initial intensity... and that's extremely rare. It took a while before I got adjusted to her lovin.' But once I did, man how we used to go at it.

I met her mom and other immediate family members who sang

my praises, but I guess it was easy to do in comparison to her ex-boyfriend. Cherry and I were like the perfect couple. The only drawback for me was her children. I was initially uncomfortable being around her daughters because Cherry and I didn't know how far our relationship was gonna go. I didn't want them getting attached to me and if things didn't work out between us I become M.I.A. like their fathers. That would be too unfair and difficult for them. Initially, Cherry understood my position and agreed, but as time transpired and our relationship blossomed, she wanted me to interact with them. I started spending the night at her house a few nights a week, but always left before dawn. I never wanted her daughters to wake up and see me there in the morning. It wasn't just about my moral fiber; I had the utmost respect for Cherry as a person and as a woman and never wanted to place her in a bad light.

You really have to be careful with girls because they easily mimic their mother's actions. So as time went on, she became comfortable with them knowing I stayed over, but for the record, I never did. I always demanded she keep her bedroom door closed even when they knew I was there. On days when she arranged for her mom or sister to babysit, she stayed at my place. Everything was going wonderfully and it almost seemed too good to be true. I guess all we needed were some challenges to really test the authenticity of our relationship.

Challenges

First, Cherry sought to test the parameters of our relationship and check for insecurities on my part. She often commented on how she didn't care for jealous men and enjoyed men who were very confident and self-secured. She told me she and her girlfriends had planned to attend a cabaret and wanted me to see the outfit she was wearing. I laughed when I saw it because I didn't take her seriously; I thought she was joking. The dress she wanted to wear looked like it was way too small for even her youngest daughter. In fact, she called it a 'move something' dress. Personally, I'd never heard or seen such a thing in my life. I ended up betting her ten dollars she couldn't fit the dress. I had no idea the dress stretched, so needless to say, I lost the bet. The dress was extremely short, low-cut and tight-fitting, and she looked sexy than a muthafucka in it. It just barely covered the crack of her ass. She told me she wasn't going to wear any underwear with it and asked what I thought about it. I pretty much figured she was testing me to see how I would handle it. "It's cool with me. Have a good time." I could tell she was a little disappointed with my calm, cool response. So she continued, "I'm probably gonna be getting in real late so I'll just call you tomorrow." "Ok, baby, just call me when you get up tomorrow morning." Then, I kissed her and left in a real good mood. You see, what Cherry didn't understand was that I was young, recently divorced and enjoying my single life so I really didn't care. Besides she wasn't my wife, just somebody I was kickin' it with. So, nothing she did was a real reflection upon me. It would've been an entirely different story if she was trying to pull that same shit as my wife. Then, I'd have probably given her the reaction she was looking for. In fact, I thought it was all kinda sexy to me; my woman going out with no underwear on in a short, tight, low-cut dress. Hell, I was fucking her real good every night so I wasn't the least bit concerned about another man. Plus, I still had my other women I was dealing with so this just gave me an opportunity to deal with one of them. So it was all good for me.

Cherry called me about 1:45 am letting me know she was home. "Hey, you sleep? I'm home." "Did you have a good time?" "It was cool. We had fun. So what did you do this evening?" I can't recall who I was with, but it was one of my girls. "Nothin' I just chilled at my place, then fell asleep. I'm glad you had a good time. I know you got rave reviews on your dress. You get a lot of phone numbers?" "About nine... but I threw them all away." "Why'd you do that?" "What do you mean why'd I do that? Because I got who I want and love who I got. Shit, I spent most of my time thinkin' bout you cause I missed yo' ass," then she chuckled. "I love you and I can't wait to see you tomorrow. I'm gone let you fuck me with my dress on." "Ooh girl you so nasty." "Mmm-hm, good night."

Weeks later I was at a gas station and saw a childhood friend who grew up in my neighborhood. We'd gone to two schools together and she'd turned out to be a fine ass grown woman. I had the deepest crush on her in elementary and was even still interested in her in high school. God damn! And she was finer than ever. Her name was Jasmine and she was the prettiest dark brown Moor (black) woman you'd ever wanna see. We exchanged pleasantries and talked for a minute before she got around to telling me she'd heard from mutual friends that I'd gotten married. I offered her the latest episode of that saga and informed her I was divorced. Man! Her eyes lit up like a Christmas tree and I knew exactly what that meant. We were going to get our long-awaited chance to get acquainted with each other and fuck. We both could sense it too. After exchanging numbers, I knew I had to tell Cherry about my intentions with Jasmine. I mean, it was only fair. I knew I was gonna end up fuckin' Jasmine and wasn't very concerned about losing Cherry in the process.

Although I really liked Cherry a lot, I wasn't pressed to maintain our relationship at all costs. I felt free enough to do whatever I wanted to do because I was no longer married and wasn't about to let any one woman inhibit me from enjoying my single life to the fullest. I figured my best everything was well ahead of me and at 26 years old, I had a whole lifetime ahead of me. So, if I lost Cherry in the process of becoming acquainted with Jasmine... fuck it. Something better would come along.

I sat Cherry down and talked to her face to face. That was another very wonderful thing about Cherry: we communicated openly and honestly. Even when it came to things she didn't necessarily wanna talk about, she was at least willing to talk. That alone is worth the price of admission. I would always sit two chairs together, facing each other, when we had controversial issues to discuss (which wasn't often). I got straight to the point. "Look Cherry, I just caught up with a girl I grew up with and we exchanged numbers. I already got the vibe that we probably gon' fuck. I've always wanted to and she's always been intrigued with me. Now that we're both finally unattached (unmarried), it looks like we're goin' in that direction." Cherry was quiet and appeared concerned, but analyzed my words.

"So... OK, when did y'all exchange numbers?" "Today." Cherry seemed a little confused. "Well, did y'all go out today or somethin'?" "Uhh-uh... we haven't gone out yet. I doubt if we even get to that." "So you haven't gone out with her yet and you already know y'all are gonna hook up?" "Yeah, it

174

was kinda a mutual vibe, I just wanted to let you know and be fair with you to give you the opportunity to deal with it. I mean, I understand if you wanna break it off, and that's your prerogative. But, I at least wanna be upfront with you before anything happened. You're my girl and I love you... and I ain't tryna hurt you. I ain't like these other niggaz out here." She looked at me with a perplexed expression in silence for a minute. She seemed relieved to know that I hadn't done anything underhanded during our relationship. That was important to her.

"I really appreciate your honesty and giving me the opportunity to make a decision. I must say, you're not like other guys I've dealt with. You could've just went on and did what you wanted to do and I probably never would've known the difference. But you were honest before the fact. So... do you love her?" "Nah! I grew up with her. She's jus' fine as hell and I've always liked her, but we never got the opportunity to talk... and basically this is our opportunity." Cherry was starting to confound me with her line of questions. "So are y'all planning to have a relationship or something?" "Naw! At least not from my perspective, but I am interested in checkin' her out... you know... I really just kinda wanna hit it." "Well, what if you fuck her and find out you really like her and wanna have a relationship?" "Cherry, I don't see all that happening. I mean, if it does, I'll have to cross that bridge when I get there." "So for you, it's just a fuck?" "Yeah, as far as I can see, but I don't know what she has in mind." Cherry nodded her head in approval of my explanation. She placed one hand on her chin and the other on her hip as she appeared to deliberate. "I tell you what..." I thought she was about to smooth curse my muthafuckin' ass out. "You just make sure you use protection... and I'll be here." Initially, I didn't understand her reply so I had her to reiterate. "I'm gonna stick and stay. I really love you and we have something very special between us. And I ain't about to lose you over a fuck. Besides, I really appreciate you bein' honest with me. I know I got your heart, so for right now, I'm willing to share yo' dick for a minute and when I ain't willing to deal with it anymore, I'll let you know. Just make sure you use protection!"

I was in utter shock, but I hid my emotions for her sake. I had absolutely no idea she was gonna say that. I was prepared to lose Cherry, but

175

she endeared herself to me for eternity with her decision. Shit! 'Cause I damn sure wouldn't have done it for her. I guess it really does pay to be honest. Now don't buy into my bullshit. Here's a real big disclaimer. Please, do not try that shit at home! Because under normal circumstances, you'll get yo' ass smooth cursed out... or worse. I was either lucky, fortunate or had initiated some good karma as a result of my true, honest intentions. Anyway, I would've never left Cherry for Jasmine. Jasmine had become what I considered a hood rat. And the more I discovered about her, the more I was glad Cherry made the decision that she did to stay with me. Jasmine lived in a storefront apartment building that was rather run down as a whole, but she kept her place surprisingly clean. From the outside, it didn't look like it was going to be a pleasant visit. She didn't have much furniture and the little she had looked liked it was from a second-hand store. She had a young son around eight years old who appeared rather withdrawn. But she later disclosed he'd been molested by one of her former boyfriends.

Jasmine was gorgeous! She was about a size 8 with tremendous breasts. She was extremely dark (like I love 'em) and had the cutest black, beauty mole on her cheekbone. She had straight whites, but one of the raggettiest tongues I'd ever seen. It was all discolored and thin like she'd been licking on sandpaper laced in acid. Jasmine, like Cherry, had very deep dimples. The one thing that stood out about Jasmine (besides her breasts) was how extremely articulate she was. She spoke the most divinely proper English I'd ever heard from a Moorish (black) woman. It was especially most notable in elementary school where we initially met. Back then Jasmine was the smallest, skinniest, darkest, prettiest, smilingest most proper-talking, smartest little girl in the world. Everybody, male and female... children and adults (Jew and Gentile, Lol!) liked her. She walked with her head up high. Actually she didn't walk. She trotted or strutted like she was royalty. She was adored by her mother and sister and they cultivated her to be a princess who would become the queen. Her mom and sister loved me as a little child. They thought we made the most beautiful little dark couple. My family liked her too and always teased me about her being my little girlfriend. I didn't mind because I had such a crush on her. Jasmine liked me as well. I always kept her laughing.

Back then, I emulated The Fonz character from the 1970s sitcom "Happy Days" (Yes, I'm embarrassed to admit it. But Fonzie was the coolest muthafucka on T.V. back then... Caucasian or Moor (black).) I only attended my neighborhood high school with Jasmine for about a year and a half and since we didn't quite run in the same circles, we didn't connect back then. We chatted in Jasmine's apartment for less than an hour during my initial visit. I was actually a little worried about my car because she lived in a real seedy part of the city where car theft was high. I kept playing it off, going to the window looking down on my car to make sure it was alright. I cut my visit short and invited her to my place that same week. In some ways, I felt a little sorry for Jasmine. She'd come from such good stock and a solid, loving family foundation. It was difficult to see her living below her means. She was starting over after a bad marriage and a rough divorce, and didn't have a whole lot. Plus, she was dealing with the molestation issue with her son. I could tell she was stressed and under a tremendous amount of pressure and really needed someone to be there for her. I noticed a pattern developing in me of attracting women with issues and/or problems. My ultra sensitivity caused me to wanna nurture these women as I assisted them in solving and resolving their issues and problems. Jasmine was just another one of those examples. Unfortunately, she dealt with the pressures of life with alcohol. Initially, I had no idea she drank so much, but it didn't take long to realize. It wasn't necessarily how much she drank more than how often... every day! Jasmine had rapidly become an alcoholic by virtue of having a drink... every day! It used to bother me when she started depending on alcohol during her stressful times. "Dayum this was a hectic day. I need a drink. I'm gonna run to the liquor store. You want something?" "Dear, you don't have to have a drink. You've gotten through the bad day now; it's all over with let's just chill out." "I plan to. I'll be right back." I knew I wouldn't be around long enough to watch Jasmine destroy herself.

One evening she came to my house tipsy and I was upset. "Why would you drive over here and you've been drinking?" "Look! I'm not drunk. I know how to handle my liquor and I don't need you tellin' me how to run my business." "Yeah, you're right. But, I care about you Jasmine and I don't want nothing bad to happen to you." "That's sweet, but I'll be O.K."

And, this was all before we got the opportunity to get together. Can you imagine? There were a few times she tried to give me some and she was tipsy. But, I don't play that shit. A woman has to be sober and in her right mind for me to be sexually involved with her. That same evening, she brought her son over and my son was already there. I couldn't help but keep a close eye on him with my son, who was only two years old. I knew that victims of molestation often acted out their experiences upon others. So needless to say, I wasn't very comfortable with her son being around mine. Call it intuition or whatever, but I was glad when LB came to pick my son up that evening. I remember the first time Jasmine and I initially engaged ourselves. It didn't work out well at all. We started kissing one afternoon and one thing led to another and clothes started coming off. Jasmine's body was real tight. She had the second biggest set of (real) breasts next to Mya's. But her vagina was a site to behold.

Imagine peeling a large grapefruit and pulling the two halves apart. Now, sit one half on the table flat side down and that's what Jasmine's vagina looked like when she was aroused. I thought she was deformed or had elephantitis of the pussy (Lol!). My eyes bugged outta my head to the point where she started explaining. "No, no wait listen! You see, I was 99 pounds when I had my son and he was a ten-pound baby. I had him through natural birth and he put so much pressure on my vagina that it turned out this way." I stared at it for about 20 minutes. I touched it like it was swollen. It was so damn big and puffy it looked like it hurt, and the more aroused she became, the larger it got (oh my God!). "Well, does it hurt?" She laughed in amusement, "No baby it doesn't hurt. It's O.K. Everybody has the same reaction when they see it." Of course, that was no consolation to me. Not only was I shocked and amazed, I was a little intimidated too. If Mya had the largest breasts I'd ever seen, the award for the largest vagina would go to... and the winner is... Jasmine! Needless to say, we didn't engage that night. I used the excuse that I didn't have any condoms.

Cherry kept asking if I'd fucked Jasmine yet, which actually got on my nerves. But Jasmine and I cultivated our intimacy over time. It took a few weeks before I was comfortable enough to attempt it again. This time, we

178

were in my living room and for some reason, Jasmine was real eager. It was almost like she wanted me to hurry up and get in so my mind wouldn't be focused upon her monster pussy. When I reclined on the floor (butt-naked), she jumped on top of me and started bouncing up and down on me hard and fast. She sounded like a porno star, "Ooh ahh, oh baby, oh baby, oh baby!" I was appalled. You mean to tell me I'd waited all these years to get with Jasmine and this is what I'd waited for?

I have to admit, I sometimes have difficulty hiding my facial expressions and she must have read my mind because as she was fucking me (like a rabbit with a double shot of espresso), she started questioning me. "What's wrong baby? Is it good? Do you like it?" "Uhh yeah... I like it." But actually, she was hurtin' the shit outta me bouncing up and down on top of me like she was on a pogo stick. "Am I pretty? Do you think I'm pretty?" Do you think I'm pretty? Now what kind of question is that for a gorgeous woman to ask during sex? I instantly felt sorry for Jasmine and in that question I read her entire life up to that point. It flashed before my very eyes. Jasmine had been dogged and taken advantage of by the men in her life. This included her ex-husband and several of her preceding boyfriends. She'd been wonderfully nurtured and cultivated as a child by her mother and sister, but never by a man... in her adult life. If there's one thing I can't stand it's a woman with low self-esteem. It's a total turn off, especially with women as gorgeously beautiful as Jasmine. I mean, what could a man have said to her, done to her, or placed in her psyche to make her see something other than what she should've seen in the mirror? I actually had to convince her that she was pretty, and what she was doing felt good to me for her to continue without that look of disappointment upon her face. I must admit it was very different.

That was the gist of my affair with Jasmine. But what really ended it for me was her drinking. I finally told her that she'd have to stop drinking (at least so much) for me to continue dealing with her. We had an extensive history because I'd known her all my life and I wasn't about to watch her destroy herself. Several weeks later, Jasmine called and said she was relatively sober. So, we rekindled our affair once again. This time it was a lot better. Jasmine was such a sweet woman and we got along wonderfully. She actually moved back in the same neighborhood we both grew up in (which looked like a war torn, third world existence by then) on the very same street she grew up on. I considered that a tremendous digression on her part... and I wasn't trying to digress. So, I knew we couldn't become anything but fuck buddies, good friends or a combination of the two.

The second time we got together, I spent the night over her house and the next morning as I was about to leave, I got up the nerve to try it. It was so much better than the first time. I even got up the nerve to go down on her monster pussy. I have to say that was perhaps the most interesting oral expression I ever offered. By the time I got finished detailing her gigantic vagina, I was tired as hell; it was like working a job. She'd always inquired about me goin' down on her, but I always offered her an excuse because I was very apprehensive. But since I kept talkin' shit to her about my skills she remained very intrigued. That morning as I tasted her she kept whispering her pleasure (we were trying not to wake her son), "Ooh wee, so this is what I been missing? Mmm Ooh baby, this is what you been keepin' from me? Yesss" But after our second encounter, I knew it would be our last. Her exoticness had simply worn off along with my intrigue about fucking her. Jasmine didn't possess the energy to sustain my attention. Besides as a rule, I bore easily and very quickly. So, I continued my relationship with Cherry.

After my rendezvous with Jasmine, Cherry admitted to being jealous about the whole situation (even though she'd initially offered her endorsement) and vowed she'd never do that again. You know it's kinda funny. When Cherry gave me permission to fuck around with Jasmine while maintaining our own relationship, I thought it would be the ultimate experience. But it really had the opposite effect on me. It made me value Cherry even more and wanna stay faithful to her. Now don't get me wrong, I took advantage of the situation, but I didn't have the fun I thought I'd have. It seemed like Cherry took all the fun out of it when she endorsed it. Well unfortunately, the opposite occurred when she clamped down on me. "All right niggah, you don' had your fun. That was yo' first and last time havin' yo' cake and eatin' it too. From now on it's me and you... exclusive... like we were before. Now, I don't want no shit outta you 'cause that was a one time thing." Now why did she have to go and say all that? Even though we were exclusive prior to Jasmine, it was unwritten. We never said we were exclusive. We just were... and I appreciated that. I felt free even though I was attached. But her proclamation made me feel kinda claustrophobic and man do I hate feeling trapped, weighed down or held back. Actually, verbalizing her desire for exclusivity made me wanna fuck around. So I did.

It was mid-summer and there was something very sensual in the air, to the point where I was feelin' my own sexy and every woman around me could feel it too. I've come to learn that women love a self-assured, confident man and I had a boat load of both. I started calling Moonbeam again and unlike after our initial fling, she was receptive to me. It just so happened she was having car trouble so I volunteered to pick her up from work. She was working at a nursing home and got off between 8:30 and 9 o'clock nightly. Moonbeam had changed. She seemed more mature and kind of seasoned too. She was definitely making better money. In the past, I found it kinda difficult taking her seriously as she worked full time at a Rite-Aid; that's a teenager's full time job, not an adult's. Moonbeam had even picked up a sexy disposition from somewhere and all that made me wanna test the waters again (and ride the waves if she allowed me). She was so thankful that I picked her up from work the first time she actually tried to offer me money as I dropped her off. It was a nice gesture, but I didn't accept it because I was financially comfortable. Shit, I had 3 jobs . So financially speaking, I was on top of the world. Plus, I wanted Moonbeam to ride in my new car anyway. She was so impressed.

Every night I dropped her off at home we'd converse a little, but not too much. I didn't want her to think I was on the prowl, even though I was. I had just the right amount of patience and savoir faire because with Cherry as my main Jane, I never had to rush or press the issue with Moonbeam. And, I know that intrigued the shit outta her because on more than one occasion, she asked if I had a girlfriend. I could tell she was starting to crave me though she never verbalized it. That just wasn't her style; it wasn't in her make up. She was a lady to her heart. But despite attempts to hide her true desires about me and us, her body language subtly said it all.

Meanwhile also during that time, my friend Angel who lived in my apartment complex was clawing at me, so I let her have it once or twice. Shit, even LB wanted some, despite the fact we were constantly at odds for one reason or another. I can't lie. I let her have it once for old time sake. Fellas, ain't it wonderful feelin' your own sexy while every woman around you is feeling it too? Doesn't it make you feel like... a god? All this was happening right under Cherry's nose and she never suspected a thing. We were still blending honey about four days a week with the intensity of a hurricane.

I started priming Moonbeam for my proposition and she was more than ready to respond. One night as I dropped her off, I hinted about us getting together. She tried to remain nonchalant as she answered yes, but I could tell she was anxious. I was too. I loved the new and improved version of Moonbeam. We'd become pretty chummy over the few weeks we'd gotten reacquainted. We talked on the phone rather consistently and our conversations were free-flowing and void of pressure. We really enjoyed each other's company and conversation, almost like something serious could develop between us. I mean, Moonbeam still didn't have any children and she had a real decent set of morals. So, I can't say I didn't contemplate whether or not she was an upgrade from Cherry. That was certainly one of my consistent character qualities.

I was always looking for an upgrade in all things and the next best thing as it related to women. But there was something about Moonbeam that made me feel like we could really have a serious relationship, if the situation was just right. I reached over and kissed her before she got out of the car and she responded favorably. She wanted me to come in and romance her, but I couldn't because I was due to see Cherry that night. But, that seemed to make Moonbeam desire me all the more. "Are you sure you don't wanna come up jus' for a lil' while?" "Babe, if I come up right now, I'm not leaving 'til the morning. I can feel it." "Me too. I don't have to be to work 'till noon." "I know honey, but I have to be in at 8 o'clock sharp. How about tomorrow night after you get off work?" "Ok... and you'll pick me up?" "Yeah of course, doll." She reached over and kissed me one last time. "I'm really lookin' forward to tomorrow." I watched her plump lil' ass as she walked into her apartment complex. She looked back and waved after she entered the front door. I was so aroused I had to tilt up the steering wheel to drive home.

I woke up the next morning excited about my plans with Moonbeam. In fact, it motivated me the entire day, to the point where time practically flew by. I went straight over to Cherry's house right after I got off work so I could make my appearance. I arrived around 5:30 pm. She'd fixed dinner and we all sat and ate like one big happy family. I was so over anxious to get with Moonbeam I couldn't wait to leave. Now, she didn't get off until 9 pm so ideally, I could've left at 8:45 to pick her up. Unfortunately, it would be my anxiousness that would be my demise. I started my routine just a little too early. At around 7:45 pm, I released an authentic yawn, "Whew... I'm gettin' a little sleepy." "Sleepy? It ain't even 8 o'clock yet." "I know, but they worked me like a Hebrew slave today and I'm tired as hell." "Well why don't you go back there and lay down for a while?" "Nah baby, I'd rather just go on home." Cherry looked at me like something wasn't quite right, but she couldn't put her finger on what it was. "Yeah... ok. Well just call me when you get home." "Alright, babe." So, I kissed her and left. We only lived about six minutes from each other. So, I called her a few minutes after eight as I arrived home. Cherry called me back around 8:20, no doubt to check up on me because she knew something was up. So I mustered up my best sleepy voice to answer the phone. "Hey baby... you asleep yet?" "Yeah, I'm dozin' off now."

"Hmm... ok. I guess I'll just talk to you tomorrow then." I could tell in her voice she wasn't quite convinced and she was also a little perturbed. Now, my spirit told me not to leave 'till 8:50 pm to pick up Moonbeam... but my (premature) erection told me to leave right after I hung up from Cherry. Ahh yes, youth... it's wasted on the young. Here's a bit of advice to you young lions: Always listen to your spirit over your penis.

Anyway, I left at 8:25 pm to pick up Moonbeam. Man, I was so fuckin' excited I sped all the way there and she only worked about twelve minutes away from me. I got there in just enough time to... wait. [You see, I always had to wait a minimum of at least a few minutes whenever I picked up Moonbeam from work. Her job required a roll call with the incoming shift].

Now keep in mind, she didn't get off until nine o'clock. So in actuality, I could've left my place at nine o'clock to pick her up, driven slowly, and I still would've had to wait a minimum of five minutes. Now if I'd been thinking clearly, I could've told her to call me when she was just about ready to walk out. That way, I could've stayed home a little bit longer to see if Cherry would call again or pop by on an unexpected visit. I sorta felt like she was gonna do one or the other, so I was prepared for it. Besides, even if I were a little late picking her up, Moonbeam could've waited a few minutes. Shit, I was her ride home so it wasn't like she was gonna leave if I wasn't there right on time. But, I'm just retracing my mistakes, which is how I learn from them.

Well unfortunately, on this particular night Moonbeam came out much later than usual. Here I was anxious to pick her up while I was at home; then, once I got there I became anxious to hurry back home to prepare for a possible Cherry sighting. Moonbeam didn't come out until 9:30 and by then I was slightly irritated... but not at Moonbeam. My irritation was due to my impatience and the fact that my impatience caused me to leave home earlier than I anticipated. So, I was irritated and embarrassed that I'd placed myself in a situation which caused my own anxiety.

Moonbeam could feel my tension as she got in the car grinning from ear to ear. "Hey baby!" My somber response quickly faded her smile, "Hey." "Uhh... I'm sorry I'm so late coming out, but I had soooo much to do before I left." We drove in complete silence for a few minutes then I eventually softened and warmed up to Moonbeam as we talked during the ride home. But for some reason I wasn't quite comfortable conversing on the way to my place because I had a strong feeling Cherry was gonna make a surprise visit. By the time I turned onto my block we were amped up and ready to go. But unfortunately as I parked, I saw Cherry's car turning around the back side of my apartment complex. You see, the way my apartment was situated you could drive all the way around the building in a complete circle. Now, I'd prepared for Cherry to pop by, but I didn't anticipate it would be before I made it back home... and into my apartment. Shit! I had to think real damn fast because in less than ten seconds Cherry would've driven the entire circumference of the building to where we were parked. So, I had to think up a super-duper, mega explanation (i.e. a bold-faced lie), quick, fast and in a hurry.

"Oh shit!" "What's wrong baby?" "I just saw my ex-wife driving around the building." Moonbeam looked confused, "But I thought y'all were divorced?" "We are honey." "Ok, then why should it matter if you're with somebody? "Uhh... because she's still bitter over me divorcing her... and uhh... she may go down to friends of the court and have my child support increased... you know, out of sheer spite." "But she can't do that. Can she?" "Technically speaking, she shouldn't be able to do that. But down there, men usually don't stand much of a chance. So it's very possible. Trust me, I've heard many guys talk about it." "Oh no, so what are we gon' do?"

I quickly took my apartment key off my key ring (as it hung from the ignition) and slid it to Moonbeam. By that time, Cherry had driven around and parked right in front of the building. She saw us in the car and waited for me to get out and walk past her car to enter my apartment complex. She'd strategically parked her car in a place where we'd have to walk past her to go inside. Moonbeam looked real concerned. "Now she ain't gon' get violent is she?" "Nah babe, she ain't jealous like that... just spiteful. Now listen real carefully and do exactly as I say. I want you to get out of the car and walk very casually... and just before you get to her car, turn around to me and say, "Thanks for the ride," but don't look at her or even look at her car. Then, go to apartment 201 and let yourself in. Now, Moonbeam had to follow my instructions precisely to avoid possibly getting her ass whooped because Cherry had the capacity to get real ghetto and she did live on the east side, which was a dangerous combination (don't worry if you don't understand; it's an inside joke only Detroiters would understand). But most importantly, if Moonbeam looked at Cherry she would've realized she wasn't my ex-wife and everything would've gotten even shittier from there.

So, Moonbeam followed my instructions to the letter and after I watched her walk (safely) past Cherry's car into the building, I got out. I stayed calm, cool and collected as I casually walked up to Cherry's car. She rolled down her window, "Niggah, where you been? I thought you were sleep, wit' cho' lying ass. See there, I knew some shit wasn't right." "Hold on! Hold on! What are you talkin' about? I was asleep until my girl Angel called me to come pick her up from work because her car broke down." "And, who the fuck is Angel?" "You know, my friend Angel who lives in the building, the one who helped me find this apartment." "Well, why didn't she call her man or one of her girlfriends to pick her up?" I chuckled, "How am I supposed to know, Cherry? I guess she called me because we both live in the same building... it makes sense to me (then I gave her the duh expression). What was I supposed to do, say no? She's one of my best friends, shit she'd do the same for me."

Cherry paused for a minute because my explanation was very believable. I impressed myself; it was quite ingénues especially considering I thought it all up in about eight seconds. I had her and I could tell by her response, "Oh really now?" Then, before she could decipher anything else, I had to get her outta there. So I played it off and looked in the back seat. "Where are the girls?" "At home." "Who's there with 'em?" "They're there by themselves... asleep." This was a perfect distraction. "By themselves, why didn't you bring them with you?" "They'll be alright until I get back, I just drove over here to see if yo' ass was home since you wasn't answering yo' phone when I called. How come you couldn't answer my calls but you managed to answer her phone call?" "Well, did you leave a message?" "Naw! Why would I leave a damn message? I didn't wanna talk to yo' answering machine; I wanted to talk to you. "Well, Angel left a message and that's what woke me up. Cherry looked sorta sheepish because it all sounded legitimate, but she wasn't thoroughly convinced. "Mmm-hmm. Whatever. So what if I come up and check your apartment?" "That's up to you." I knew she wasn't really going to because she had to get back home to her girls. She just wanted to see my response so I called her bluff. Trust me, if it wasn't for the fact that I remained so cool and calm she probably would've came in. "Mmm-hmm...alright niggah, I'm gon' talk to you in a few minutes when I get home. And you better answer the phone!" "Yeah, ok." Then she drove off... and I gladly waved goodbye to her. But, it wasn't over yet.

I went in and buzzed my apartment number for Moonbeam to let me in because she had my key. When I came in, she was sitting on my couch still wearing her sweater. "Is everything alright?" Moonbeam was so gullible. She had absolutely no idea what was going on and took me at my word. "Yeah, she's all good now." I told Moonbeam to take her sweater off and make herself at home. In the meantime, I went in my bedroom and called (the real) Angel and asked her to do me a possible favor. I told her what happened and that I wanted to have a game plan if Cherry decided to come back and do a walk through of my apartment. I asked Angel to let Moonbeam chill at her apartment for a few minutes if Cherry comes back to check my place. Angel just laughed like she usually did and said it was ok. She thought it was funny. That's why Angel was my home girl. She was an all-in-one, all-encompassing friend. Angel was anything and everything I needed her to be. And at that time, I needed Angel to be the friend to hide my girl... from my girlfriend. But unfortunately, Moonbeam and I didn't get a chance to share passion because she got spooked and requested that I take her home. I had to wait for Cherry to call first then I took her home. Moonbeam suggested that we share passion at her apartment. But I declined 'cause I didn't wanna hear Cherry's naggin', and bitchin', if she called or came by and I wasn't there. Plus, that would've nullified my lie she'd already accepted as true. I was so disappointed! That was also the last time I ever saw or heard from Moonbeam. I guess I had just too much drama goin' on for her.

As it had become my custom, I indoctrinated Cherry with church, GOD and biblical principles. I must say, she showed more respect for those things than most church women. Cherry wasn't the least bit religious, but respected the fact that I was and sympathized with my struggle to maintain my morality. At one point, she expressed her sentiments, "You make me feel so bad after we make love... how you be feelin' so guilty afterward. It's hard for me watching you go through that. It's like I'm causing you to sin. Do you think we should stop?" "I know we should, but you're so much a part of me now. I don't want to." One night after one of her let's-get-married tirades, I suggested to her that there may have been another reason why our paths crossed. We had a real long, deep discussion about GOD and relative issues. She was mesmerized listening to me like I was the Pope (Lol!). Then she came to a conclusion that maybe I entered her life to bring her into a knowledge of GOD. "I know that I'm an angel on assignment for the Lord to bring the message of salvation to all who'll receive it... and maybe that was all I was supposed to do. But we got caught up in the physical thang." Her eyes watered as she listened intently in silence. Then we stood up and hugged each other for a long time... slowly and simultaneously twisting from side to side. It felt so eerie. We sat back down on the couch in silence and held hands. She looked at me and smiled. It was obvious we'd bonded in that moment and it felt so intimate.

In weeks prior we'd talked about anal sex (how she'd never done it but always wanted to try it) and somehow our conversation flowed in that direction. Yeah, I know it was a strange segway from the religious conversation we'd had minutes before. But sometimes real, true-to-life accounts are that way. We were sitting in the dark when I tossed two of her couch pillows on the floor. She already knew what was next, so she stood up and pulled her sweat pants off. She didn't have any panties on, which immediately increased the erection I already had. She'd just bathed before our initial conversation and had been lotioning her feet, so the lubricant was already conveniently located. I squirted a shot of lotion in my hand and massaged it on my dick. In the meantime, she got on all fours placing her knees on the pillows. She was already making passionate sounds. I gently and sensually rubbed the excess lotion on her ass and around her anal canal; she loved it.

Cherry was so passionate and feminine. She always instinctively knew how to take our intimate moments to the highest level of sensuality. I got on my knees behind her and inserted myself... just a little. I definitely wanted to be considerate especially since it was her first time. But surprisingly, she was so hot and ready for it (and the mood was just right), she took it like a champ, so I eased in a little more. I don't know why anal sex has the tendency to bring out my sadistic side, but it does. So I softly grabbed one of her shoulders for better balance and leverage. Cherry wanted me to scratch her. In fact, whenever she straddled me or we did it doggie style, she'd always tell me to scratch her butt. I mean, real hard too... sometimes to the point where she would damn near bleed. Then later I'd pick her skin from under my fingernails. Hold on now, don't think something's wrong with me because I gave her what she wanted   She was moaning so loud, I was glad her daughters weren't home. The more she moaned, the further I advanced.   I grabbed a hand full of her hair and pulled her head back towards me until her nose pointed toward the ceiling   Cherry loved that kinda shit and because she did, I loved it too   You know the old saying, 'if you like it I love it?' Well, there you have it. It was all just soooo sexy that it wasn't long before I felt the most tremendous urge to release. And, since I didn't have to pull out I just let it go GOOD GOD AL-MIGHTY...MAN it was so intense! From then on, I knew anal sex would become a normal part of our sexual repertoire.

Trouble in Cherryland

My friend Crenshow finally decided to get his driver's license (yes, at age 26) and would soon after be in the market to buy a car...nothing new... just a hooptie. For those of you who are unfamiliar with the term hooptie, it's a raggedy piece of shit car on its last leg that you must continuously repair to keep it running. Well, that's what Cherry's Ford Escort was... a hooptie. And, it was just perfect for Crenshow because that was about all he could afford to buy. Cherry's car wasn't worth $500.00. In fact, it really needed to be donated to someone. But she wasn't willing to part with her car as a donation. So, I devised a wonderful plan. I advised her if she was willing to sell her car to Crenshow for $400.00 she could have my there year old car and I'd buy myself a brand new car. Now, when I said she could have my car, I meant she could finish paying the remaining car payments and have the title once it was paid for. The monthly note was only $234.00. I purchased it brand-spankin' new in 1989 and it was only the fall of 1992. I had a year left to pay it off. So in essence, she was gonna pay less than $3000.00 for a new car that was a tremendous upgrade from her ten year old hooptie. Well, she was more than willing to accept the deal and was extremely anxious and excited about it. I started the ball rolling by leasing a new 1991 5-Series BMW, which was an upgrade from my sporty, two-door Acura. Now everybody was ecstatic because we all received tremendous upgrades in the automobile department. I got a newer, bigger car. Cherry got a much newer and bigger car and Crenshow got his very first car. Even though it was a hooptie, it was better than driving his Chevro-legs. In other words, a slow drive beats a fast walk every time.

Everything was going wonderfully. Cherry happily offered me the money for the car payment every month like clockwork. We got closer than ever... to the point where she regularly talked about marriage. But every time she brought up the subject, I reminded her of my recent divorce and told her I wasn't looking to remarry no time soon. But it only seemed to register for a short period of time and after a couple a weeks, she was at it again. During this time Cherry started receiving phone calls from her old boyfriend, her youngest daughter's father... yeah, the one who whooped her ass and threw her and his daughter out on the street. "Why is he calling you so much?" "I don't know. He's been askin' how I was doin' and saying he'd been thinkin' bout me." "Really now?" "Yeah... that's the same thing I said to myself." Then one day as we were working on her front lawn, she saw him drive by, which was strange because he lived way across town. I guess we must've looked like one big happy family because her daughters were playing in the yard and everything.

Well at that point I knew what was going on and attempted to inform Cherry. "That Niggah saw our new cars in your driveway and a man at your house and knows you're doing real well for yourself without his ass. Now he's starting to call you because he's trying to see where your head is concerning him." "Uhh-huh I know, well he ain't got shit coming with me... not after the way he did me." As time went on, she saw him riding down her street more frequently. One evening he called and she wore a strange expression on her face as she listened. She covered the phone with one hand, "It's Vance and he's crying on the phone?" "He's crying? Why, did somebody kick his ass?" "Noooo silly, (showing frustration with me) he's saying he wants me back." I thought to myself... why is she even having a conversation with this guy? She almost appeared to be entertaining the thought.

I stayed over Cherry's house that night and our love-making was perhaps the most intense it had ever been. But something told me to go home afterward. I ignored that something and the next morning as I was about to unlock my car door to drive home I saw the lock had been blown out... and the door was ajar. I looked through the window to see the radio was gone. When I got in the car, it became abundantly clear that whoever stole my radio was very careful not to damage anything. Everything was neatly dismantled and very professionally done; almost like they were sending a message. Needless to say I was hot than a muthafucka! Cherry was standing at the front door observing my shock, dismay and anger. "I know it was that muthafucka who stole my goddamn radio!" "Who Van? I don't think he would've done something like that." "Why not? That Niggah was crying on the phone like a lil' bitch yesterday talkin' 'bout how he wanted you back, and you said you saw him driving down your street before then. Damn! Something told me to take my monkey ass home! The next time you talk to that punk-ass muthafucka you tell him I'm fucking him up on sight. In fact, you can show me where he lives and I can pay his ass a visit." "No, I am not gonna do that. Besides, you don't even know it was him for sure." "Why are you taking up for that muthafucka? You act like you wanna get back with his ass." I left mad as hell. Then a few weeks later, as it had become her custom, she brought up marriage again, but this time with a new twist. "Look, when are we gonna talk about getting engaged? We've been together over a year now and we're solid. What are you waiting on? I'm gonna let you know something... Vance is talking about marriage."

I was so damn mad when she said that. Not because I was jealous or anything. She just sounded like such a damned fool, entertaining the thought of getting back with a niggah who beat the shit outta her and threw her and his own daughter out on the street. I was actually embarrassed for her. And, she had the unmitigated gall to say it like she was proud too. I looked at her like she was crazy. "And!? So what! You sound stupid for even saying some dumb-ass shit like that. After what he did to you?" Then she looked a little embarrassed and retorted. "Well, I'm just saying at least he's looking to get married." A week or so later she offered me an ultimatum. "Look I ain't trying to pressure you, but if you ain't looking to at least get engaged within the next few months, something's gotta

191

give. 'Cause I ain't getting no younger." Now that was the last straw for me. "Hey, hey wait a minute! Don't give me no fuckin' ultimatums. And why are you so in a hurry to get married anyway? Now I don' told you, I'm just getting divorced good and I ain't about to let you or nobody else pressure me into getting married prematurely. So, if you can't wait till I'm ready then do what you need to do." "Ok, I will. So what about the car?" "What about it? You'll still get the car because you paid for it... and that's whether we're together or not." "But how do I know you're really gonna give me the title?" I suddenly realized it wasn't Cherry talking... it was ol' punk ass Vance speaking through her. "Well I guess you gone just have to trust me, huh!"

From that time on, Cherry and I was no longer an item. It was like she had become someone else... and I didn't like the new her. It was so strange how she became so expendable to me after that incident. I didn't think twice about letting her go even after all the good love we made, all the long talks we had and all the good times we shared. Un-fuckin-believable! I didn't even look forward to seeing her when she dropped off money for the car note, although I definitely looked forward to receiving the money. On the day I made the final car payment, she absolutely tore her ass with me. I'll never forget it. I told her I'd bring the title to the car once I had it in my possession. Do you know what that heafa said? "I wanna trail you to the finance office because I don't really trust you." I couldn't believe her... after all this time. I would've been hurt if I wasn't so pissed.

Cherry trailed me out to the car finance company and actually followed me in the building. Like what was I gonna do, run away on foot once I got the title? She even tried to go to the window with me as I made the last payment. That's when she'd gone too far. I told her to wait until I finished transacting the business. She actually made a little scene and everything, which really sealed her fate with me because I don't tolerate public embarrassment. I had to inform her stupid ass that sub-leasing a car, which is what I'd done, was totally illegal. "Cherry, you gon' fuck around and neither of us are gonna get this damn car if you don't let me transact this business." So she stood back, but damn-near hovered over my shoulder the whole time, which of course irritated the shit outta me. Once I gave the money to the teller, Cherry swooped up to the window like she was the police. As the teller was about to hand me the title, Cherry stuck her hand under the glass to intercept it. When she did that me and the teller looked at her like... What the fuck are you doing? "Excuse me ma'am, but he has to proofread all the information on the title to make sure it's correct. Sir, is she with you?" I was so mad and embarrassed I didn't know what to do.

Once I'd transacted all the business and obtained the title, I walked outside. Cherry walked so close behind me that she kept stepping on my heels. Once we got right outside the door, I turned around and handed her the title and she seemed shocked. "Wow! You really gave it to me." I didn't say a word. I just shook my head in disbelief and walked away from her. She ran and stepped in front of me, "Wait a minute. What's wrong?" "Hey you got the title, so now wha' 'chu want?!" "Why are you acting like that? Is it because of Vance?" I was at the pinnacle of my pisstivity. Cherry just didn't get it. "Are you serious...are you fuckin' kidding me? Naw bitch, it ain't 'got nothin' na do with him. It's 'YOU! How the fuck you gon' say you don't trust me, when all I've ever tried to do is help yo' monkey ass? This car is just one example of that." "I'm sorry it was Van, he kept telling me you might not give me the car once you and I broke up and I listened to him." "But the mere fact that you're listenin' to the same muthafucka who whooped yo' ass and threw you and his daughter out on the street, is the stupidest shit I've ever heard of in my entire life. So do me a real big favor Cherry. Lose my phone number and don't you EVER call me again! You got that?! I don't even want chu' as a friend at this point! If you're that damn desperate to get married, then I wasn't the one for you anyway. I don't want a woman who just wants to get married. I want a woman who wants to marry ME! And there's a hell-of-a difference between the two!" By the time I finished going off on Cherry, tears were streaming down her face. But I didn't care, not because I was insensitive... rather because she was so fuckin' stupid!

Goin' Off, After What Went On

Its incredible how utterly selfish you can be
Oftentimes so arrogant to the highest degree
How tremendously ungrateful you have been unto me
And your own foolish pride blinds you to see.

I've taken care of your every need
And a great many of your wants
You've never lacked any necessity
You've had your choice of three cars to drive
They belonged to ME, before becoming 'yours and mine'
But you ride so indignantly...the nerve of your audacity

When you flick a light switch...the bulb illuminates
When you turn a faucet handle...you see the water flow
When you adjust the thermostat...it gets warmer
When the telephone rings...you just answer and say hello

I've opened my home, my heart and so much more
To you and your five kids
But all you complain about is what I don't do and haven't done
Instead of all the wonderful things I did

I was the sole investor in YOUR business
Which you were reluctant to make me a part of
I damn near ruined my credit to make sure you'd get it
I guess money can't buy me love?

And all this, without you contributing a dime
Believe me honey it's all good and fine
Your happiness is my greatest concern
Often times at the risk of relinquishing mine

When you're happy our union is blissful
And you tout me as the greatest man on earth
But when you're sad, mad or anything but glad
Your tantrums and attitudes nullify my worth

Throwing fits and slamming doors because I speak my mind?
Then baby, we're gonna clash almost every time
Even though you reign supreme
You won't dictate my emotions and harness my opinion
Yes, you're the Goddess that I worship with my praise
But you don't define my manhood.
Can't you rule our royal kingdom without governing my dominion?
Sleeping on the edge of the bed
Because you don't wanna be touched
I refused to carry on that way
I don't like being in love that much

Learn to disagree without being disagreeable
Anything less is showing contempt and disrespect
Just hear me out, even when you don't feel like listening
Or all the negativity you offer me is exactly what you're gonna get.

Please understand something very crucial
Before you and your crew boarded this ship it was just me and my son

So realize this, one person adjusting to six personalities
Is much more difficult than six people adjusting to one

Why can't you simply acknowledge me?
Or at least act like you do
Otherwise, I'll be the enemy of whomever you listen to
And it doesn't matter who that is
Cause if they don't pay our bills or sleep with us
They're opinions over mine aren't anything you should trust

At this point in my life patience wasn't my great virtue, especially in areas of dealing with the 'weaker vessel'. First of all, I thought 'they' needed a much better handle on controlling 'their' emotions, which in my opinion made them the opposite of man and thus, the opposition to man. I really disliked and sometimes loathed women's emotionalities, unless of course it worked in my favor like when I was seducing them. Then it was ok because I was getting something out of the deal. In my estimation men were seemingly cooler, calmer, and more calculating in their mental approach to relationships. I just didn't see many examples of men having those subtle emotional break downs that so many women appeared to suffer.

Secondly was it just my imagination, or were the women I experienced very inept, gullible, vulnerable, insecure, and easy? Back then women were so expendable to me, especially since I was divorced, single and so ready to mingle. I felt so free and there were just too many women to choose from. I appeared to attract them pretty effortlessly. It was like finding pennies on the street, I could find 15 cents within a quarter of a mile.

I wasn't quite a 'one woman man' during that time. In fact, I corralled several different women together to equal my version of a complete woman. I had one woman who was funny and made me laugh, another woman who was intelligent and mentally stimulating, a third woman who 'blended honey' just the way I liked, another woman as my confidant and friend, so forth and so on. You get the picture?

They just needed to be properly trained on how to love, honor, respect, and serve the 'stronger vessel' (ME). Speaking of respect, I've always found it difficult to value anybody I didn't respect. Unfortunately for the female gender at this time in my life, I didn't have high regard for women in general and especially for the women in my sphere. They just didn't offer much challenge. It was all just too easy...almost boring. I'd always heard about the women who could break men down and have 'em crying over them. But in my experience that kind of women was like the legend of 'bigfoot,' just a myth...something other people reported, or something you hear about from other people but never see or experience yourself. I know for certain that I hadn't met up with 'her' scandalous ass...yet. And I figured I'd be well able to identify her if I ever did. My Aunt Mary use to say, "Just keep living." I figured her saying meant that if I kept living, I would find a woman worthy of my respect.

***

A Personal Reflection.....

Those were my views and opinions back then, but they were merely my sentiments of that time and not a summation of my character. That's probably at least one good reason why it's best not to judge. "He among you who is without sin cast the first stone," right?

Goddess and God are complimentary and are as inseparable as any other dichotomy. Goddess and God simultaneously symbolize sister and brother, wife and husband, queen and king...female and male. A man can only revere a woman as he reveres himself because he is no more than his estimation of woman. With that being said, the sentiments and opinions of my youth regarding the female gender were a direct reflection of what I felt about myself as a man.

197

All fetuses start out female even before they become male infants. Consider the Supreme Being of the universe as a feminine energy. How might Mother Goddess respond to the misuse and abuse of her daughters by the hands of virtual genetic defects? Or even more, by someone who began as a female, was born of a female and was absolutely dependent upon a female? Well, karma just so happens to be a feminine principle that everyone experiences...negative and positive.

That reminds me a something my great aunt Mary used to always say, "Just keep living." I not only discovered what she meant (by that) on several different levels, but specifically in relation to discovering how strong the so called 'weaker vessel' actually is. But I don't want to disclose too much about it right now, I think the continuation of this epic tale will make an excellent storyline for Womb-man, Volume II. Trust me you just may need a box of tissue for this one. For as comedic and light-hearted Volume 1 was, the next promises to be equally as tragic and dramatic. Fellas, I hope you can take a lesson from it so you won't have to experience what I experienced. Until then, keep ascending!

KAI HERU

is the founder of the Wholisitc Health Awareness Team LLC, a group of naturopathic doctors and wholisitic physicians specializing in Energy Therapy and wholistic health services and products. Kai Heru is a professor and facilitator of Meridian Therapy Tapology (Breakthrough Method) and co-founder of Enlightenment Group LLC, 'paradigm shifters' whose mission is to empower, enlighten, and assist in raising the consciousness of humanity by providing essential life skills and wholistic health awareness. In addition to his poetic expressions, Kai Heru is a gifted experienced singer, stage actor and accomplished songwriter and arranger.

ARTIST, WHOLISTIC PRACTITIONER, 'PARADIGM SHIFTER'